Mel Bay's
DELUXE GUITAR ARPEGGIO STUDIES

Al Hendrickson

Art Orzeck

INTRO

This encyclopedia of guitar scales and arpeggios is modeled after the similar volume for the electric bass written by the authors in 1974. Both books, of course, were modeled after the original *Guitar Melody Playing,* by the authors, written in 1948.

The advantage of the encyclopedia over the older method is the expansion of the system to include all the practical scales and arpeggios exactly spelled out, leaving nothing for the student to figure out for himself.

This volume also presents the principal arpeggios *with* the scales, not as a separate section as was done in the earlier volume. A separate section on arpeggios is later presented in the manner of the bass encyclopedia to make the arpeggio study as completely comprehensive as possible. There are then some repetitions which are not a redundancy, but is actually a way of showing more complete relationships of the previously presented arpeggios. They are presented much like a guitar chord exposition throughout the entire range of the fingerboard.

The study of chords is entirely omitted from this volume. An encyclopedia of chords has already been excellently written by Bill Bay* and there is no point to duplication here. Furthermore, chords do not serve the end of single line melody playing, which is the purpose of this volume.

To preserve more usual musical relationships, Parts One and Two, The Scales and Principal Arpeggios, are presented according to the fifth relationship.(See the circle of Keys on page 8.) Each key is a fifth apart from its neighbor. The principal arpeggios, too, are related by the same fifth interval. Because the player may want to simply look up a scale or arpeggio, the volume is indexed by consecutive pages and alphabetically. Part Three, Comprehensive Arpeggios, is presented in a somewhat abridged form, but the player should have no difficulty constructing any arpeggio according to the models shown.

The term "position" indicates a span of four consecutive frets. The player's four fingers spans the four frets in any given position. The first finger of such a span labels the position number. (See the fifth position modeled below:)

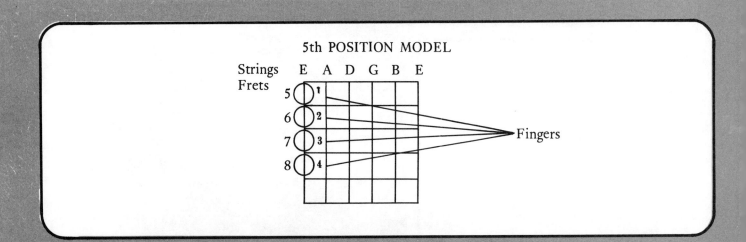

5th POSITION MODEL

*Mel Bay's Deluxe Encyclopedia of Guitar Chords, by Bill Bay, 1971.

CONTENTS

CONTENTS BY 5th RELATIONSHIP

HOW TO TUNE THE GUITAR

The student should first tune the first (E) string to the corresponding E on the piano. This E is the first E above middle C (see below). (The guitar sounds one octave lower than it reads.) Next, press the second string (B) at the fifth fret and tune it to a unison with the first string. Next, press the third string (G) at the fourth fret and tune it to a unison with the second string. Next, press the fourth string (D) at the fifth fret and tune it to a unison with the third string. Next, press the fifth string (A) at the fifth fret and tune it to a unison with the fourth string. Finally, press the sixth string (E) at the fifth fret and tune it to a unison with the fifth string. Check tuning by comparing octaves. Always tune from high to low because the higher strings are more easily heard in tune.

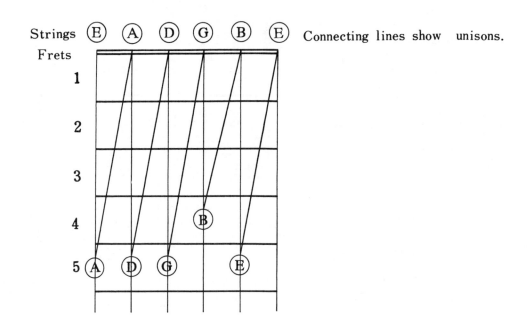

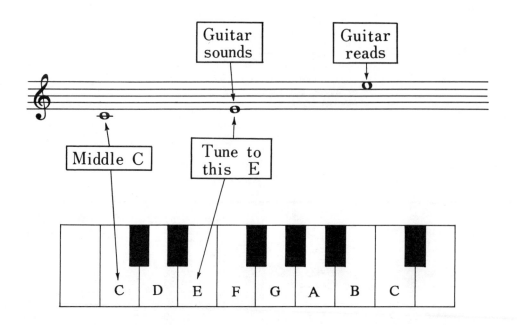

GUITAR FINGERBOARD

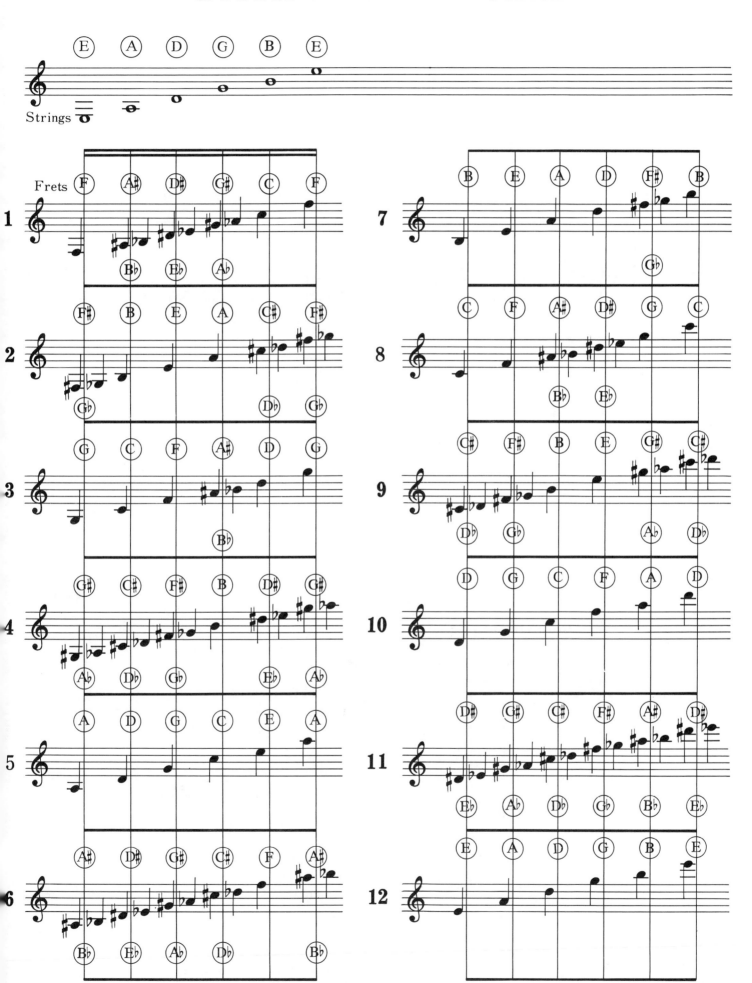

KEY FORMULA

A formula is here presented to help the player find any given key or position with respect to the four forms presented in this volume.   As the student explores the volume, this section will become very meaningful.

MAJOR FORMATIONS

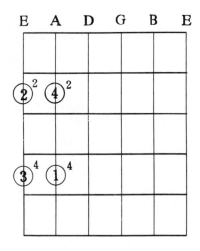

1. PRIMARY MAJOR FORMATION. Begin with the 4th finger on the A String in any given position.

2. SECONDARY MAJOR FORMATION. Begin with the 2nd finger on the E String in any given position.

3. TERTIARY MAJOR FORMATION. Begin with the 4th finger on the E String in any given position.

4. QUATERNARY MAJOR FORMATION. Begin with the 2 nd finger on the A String in any given position.

- -

MINOR FORMATIONS

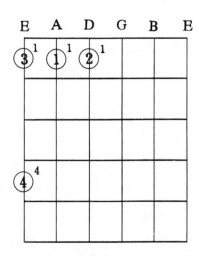

1. PRIMARY MINOR FORMATION. Begin with the Ist finger on the A String in any given position.

2. SECONDARY MINOR FORMATION. Begin with the Ist finger on the D String in any given position.

3. TERTIARY MINOR FORMATION. Begin with the Ist finger on the E String in any given position.

4. QUATERNARY MINOR FORMATION. Begin with the 4th finger on the E String in any given position.

SCALE THEORY

All fretted instruments have a fingerboard composed of half tones on a continuum. There are 12 half tones in a one octave chromatic scale (see fingerboard chart, page 5.) The scale notes have letter names (below) A B C D E F G, and are repeated octave after octave. Since some intervals between notes are <u>half tones</u> and some are <u>whole tones,</u> there are 12 half <u>tones</u> in all. For example.

Note that a <u>sharp</u> (♯) raises a given note a half tone. The same chromatic scale can use <u>flats</u> (♭) to lower any given note. See Example:

If the two are combined, a scale of <u>enharmonic equivalents</u> results.

The piano fingerboard is shown to better illustrate. Each white and black note is equal to a fret on the guitar.

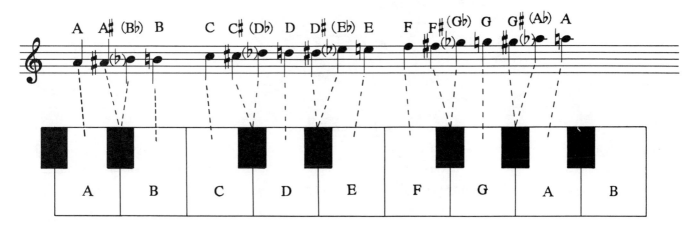

An already sharped note can be sharped again by using the <u>double sharp</u> sign (𝄪). A <u>double flat-ted</u> note employs two flats (♭♭) to achieve the same purpose when a note is to be lowered two times.

A sharp or flat can be cancelled out by using a natural sign (♮). For example to cancel G♯ a natural sign is used: To cancel out G♭ use the same natural sign.

There are basically two kinds of <u>diatonic</u> scales, <u>Major</u> and <u>Minor.</u> A diatonic scale is demonstrated by referring to the white keys on the piano. From C to C, one octave, is a major diatonic scale - C Major. From A to A, one octave, is a minor diatonic scale - A Minor. A minor scale may be altered in a variety of ways which makes it flexible and interesting. This will be demonstrated in the body of the volume.

A scale is playable in a variety of <u>key signatures.</u> While there are 12 <u>enharmonic</u> keys, most musicians accept 15, but this involves enharmonic duplication. This volume will present 13, and even then there is one duplication. See the <u>Circle of keys</u> (the Fifth Relationship) below. Neighboring keys (and the 3 fundamental harmonies of a key) are a fifth away. A fifth is five scale degrees. See Below:

Circle of Keys

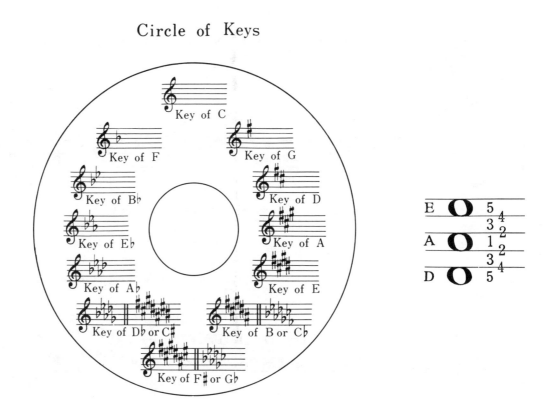

A scale may be said to be any two or more <u>contiguous</u> notes on the musical staff. Thus, C Db, or C D, is a two note scale. The simplest chord or arpeggio is any two or more notes played by <u>skip</u> on the musical staff. Thus, C Eb or C E, may be considered a two note chord when played at the same time. If these notes are played separately, they constitute an arpeggio.

Any arpeggio or chord may be altered by sharping or flatting any or all of its notes except the root which gives the chord or arpeggio its name. The most usual altered arpeggios will be presented in this volume.

Finally, while this is an encyclopedia of scales and arpeggios, it is not all of music. Every student should at least take a basic course in harmony. A dictionary of music will go a long way toward answering simple questions as they arise.

CONTROLLED PICKING EXERCISE

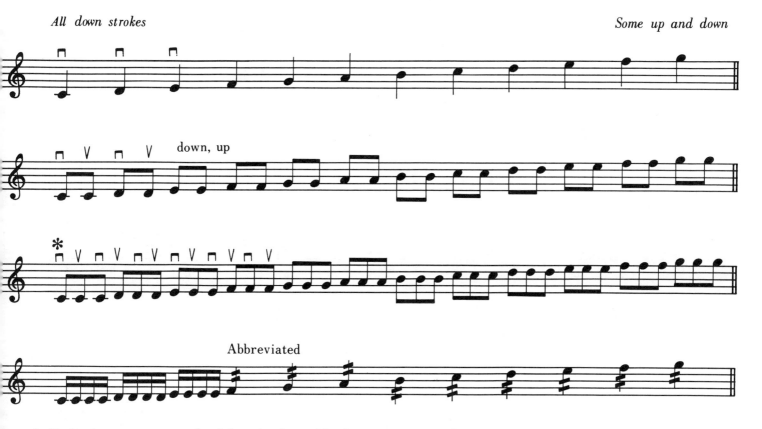

All down strokes

Some up and down

down, up

Abbreviated

✱ Each alternate group of triplets begins with the opposite stroke direction. The student must maintain the accent(first note of each group) in spite of the alternate up-stroke. Scales should be practiced going from low to high and vice versa, maintaining original evenness of rhythm throughout. It is quite simple with practice and its importance cannot be over-emphasized for the development of the right hand.

$\frac{6}{8}$ rhythm is the most common of the *compound rhythms*. The significance of the $\frac{6}{8}$ measure is this: There are 6 eighth notes per measure. Each eighth note gets $\frac{1}{3}$ rd of a beat. There are consequently two beats in each measure.

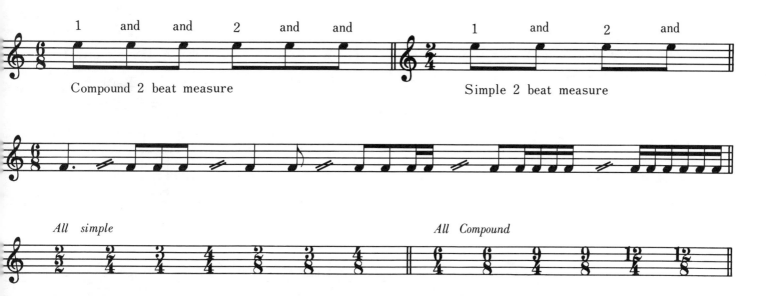

Compound 2 beat measure

Simple 2 beat measure

All simple

All Compound

The upper numeral of the compound fraction is divisible by 3 The answer is the number of beats per measure. The lower numeral is of course the type note which receives $\frac{1}{3}$ rd of a beat.

PART ONE – MAJOR FORMS

Scales and Related Arpeggios in all the positions

PRIMARY FORMS

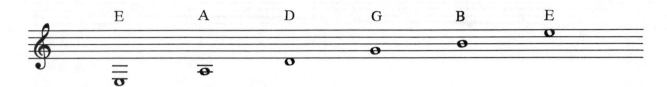

OPEN POSITION - C MAJOR

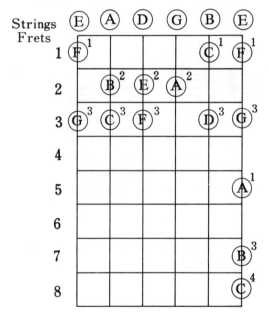

ARPEGGIOS

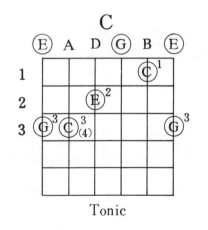

Tonic

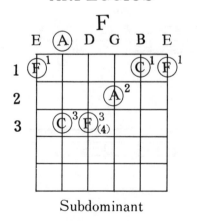

Subdominant

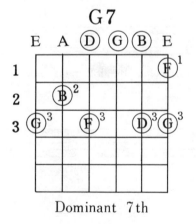

Dominant 7th

PRIMARY FORMS

Vth Position F Major

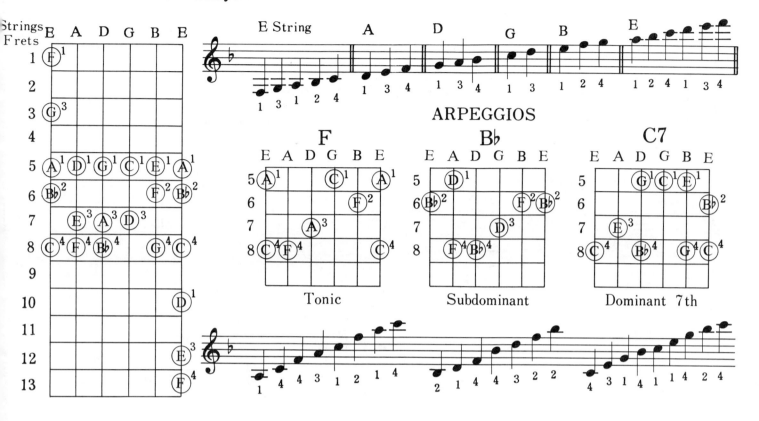

ARPEGGIOS

F — Tonic
Bb — Subdominant
C7 — Dominant 7th

VIIth Position G Major

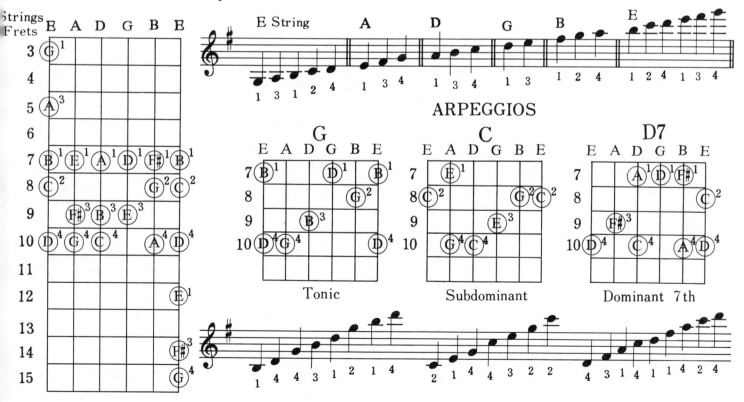

ARPEGGIOS

G — Tonic
C — Subdominant
D7 — Dominant 7th

PRIMARY FORMS

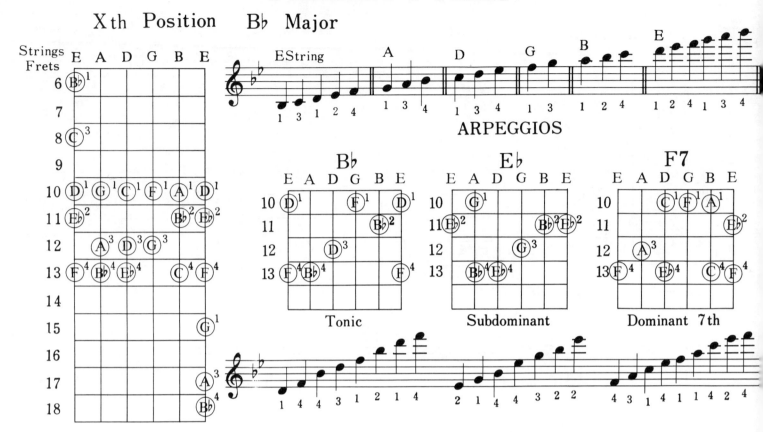

Xth Position   B♭ Major

ARPEGGIOS

B♭	E♭	F7
Tonic	Subdominant	Dominant 7th

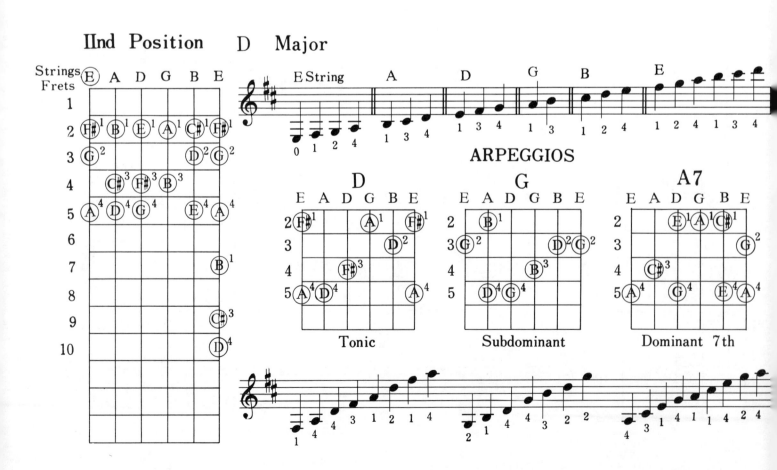

IInd Position   D Major

ARPEGGIOS

D	G	A7
Tonic	Subdominant	Dominant 7th

PRIMARY FORMS

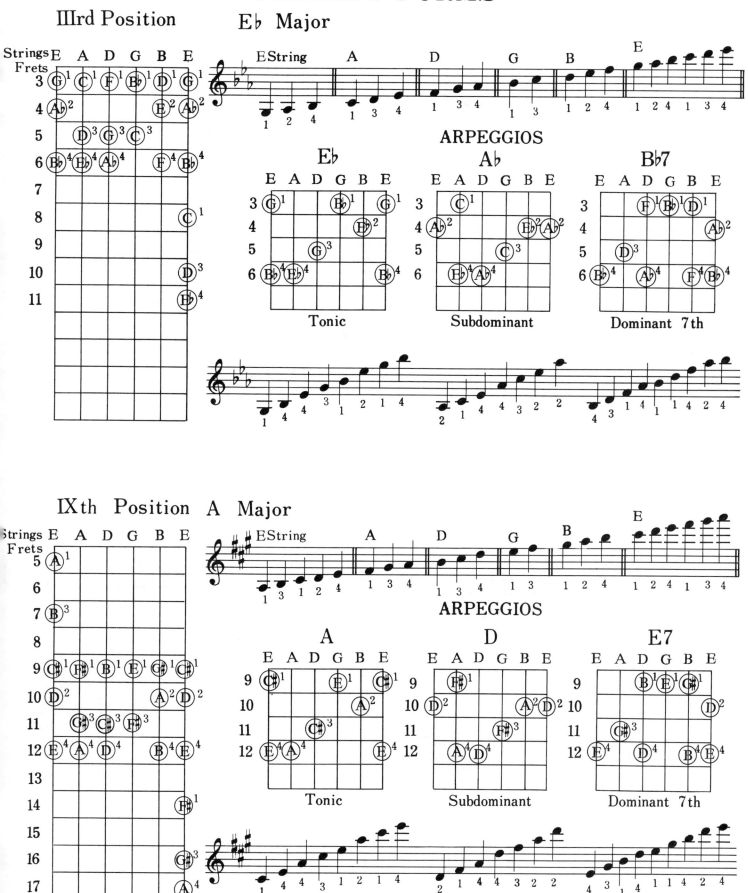

PRIMARY FORMS

VIIIth Position A♭ Major

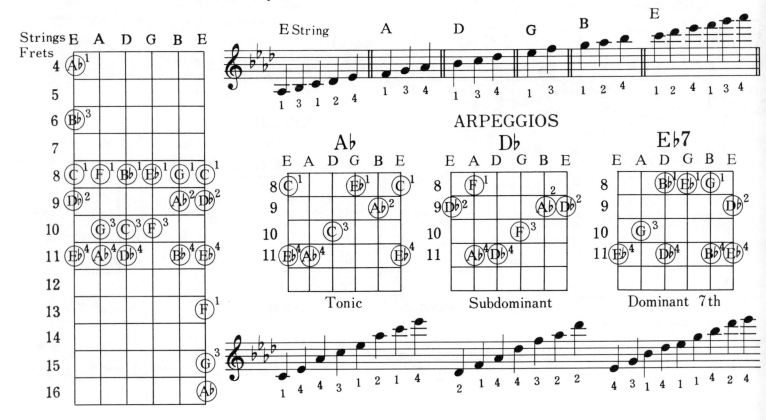

ARPEGGIOS

A♭ — Tonic
D♭ — Subdominant
E♭7 — Dominant 7th

IVth Position E Major

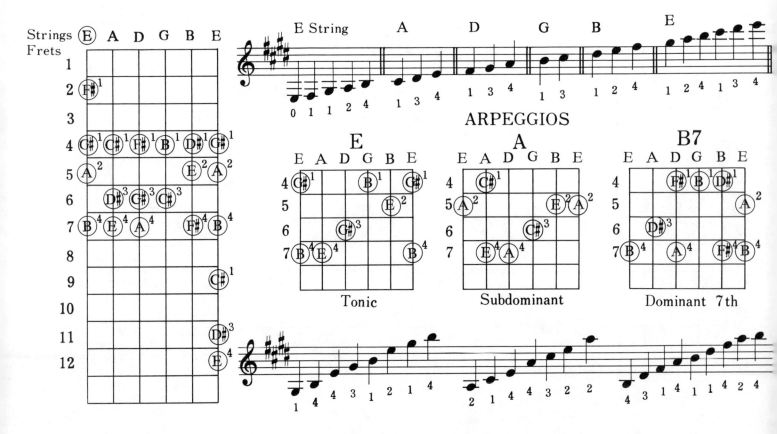

ARPEGGIOS

E — Tonic
A — Subdominant
B7 — Dominant 7th

PRIMARY FORMS

Ist Position Db Major

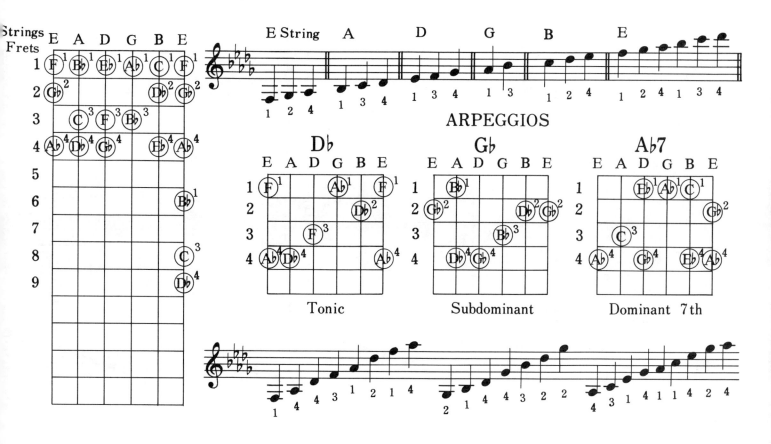

XIth Position B Major

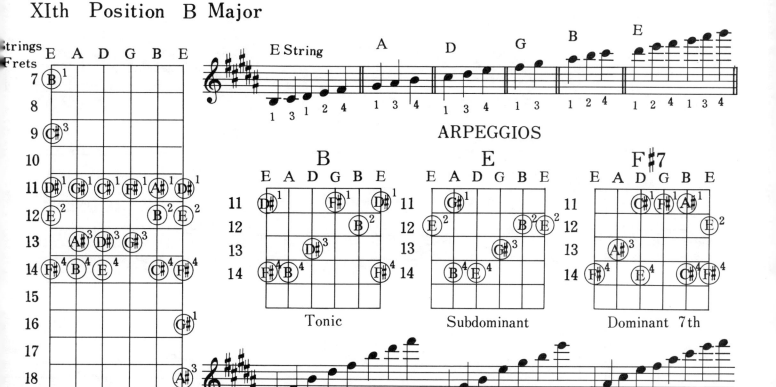

PRIMARY FORMS

VIth Position Gb Major

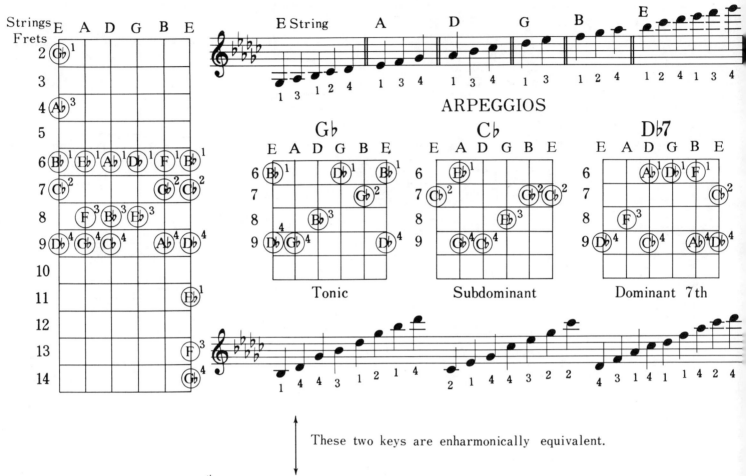

ARPEGGIOS

Gb — Tonic
Cb — Subdominant
Db7 — Dominant 7th

These two keys are enharmonically equivalent.

VIth Position F# Major

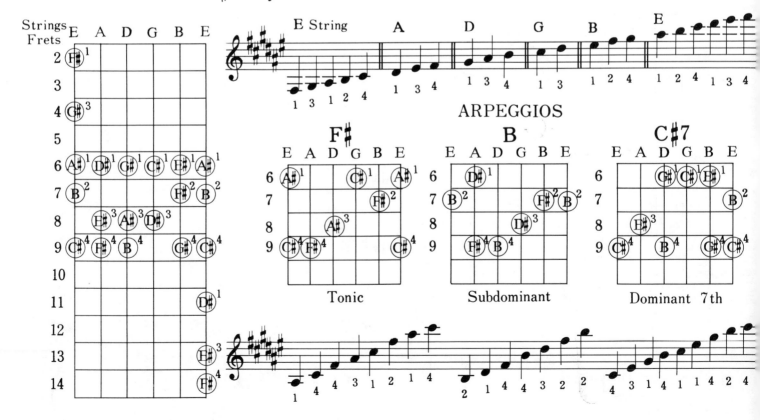

ARPEGGIOS

F# — Tonic
B — Subdominant
C#7 — Dominant 7th

SECONDARY FORMS
C Major

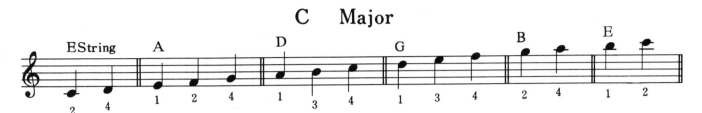

VIIth Position

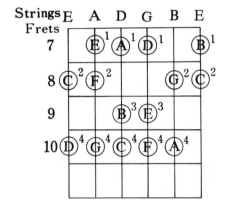

ARPEGGIOS

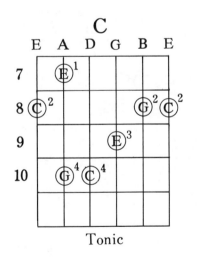
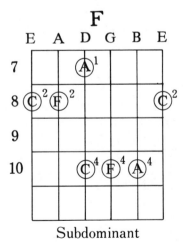
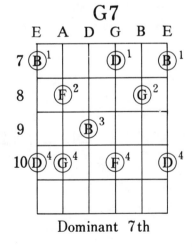

Tonic   Subdominant   Dominant 7th

SECONDARY FORMS

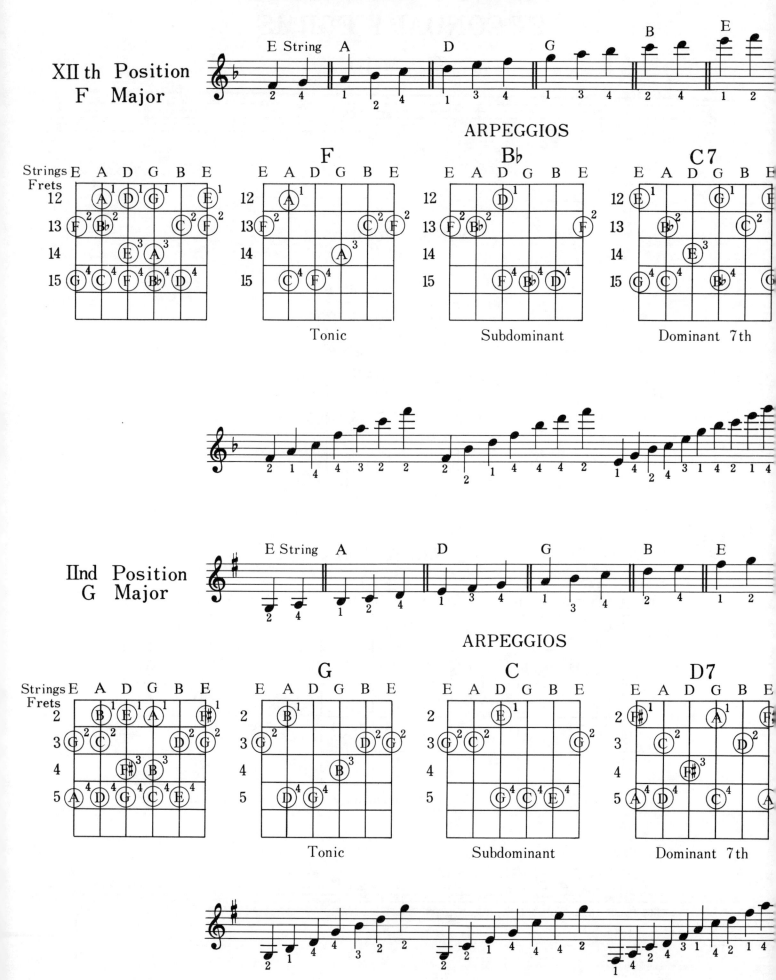

ARPEGGIOS

SECONDARY FORMS

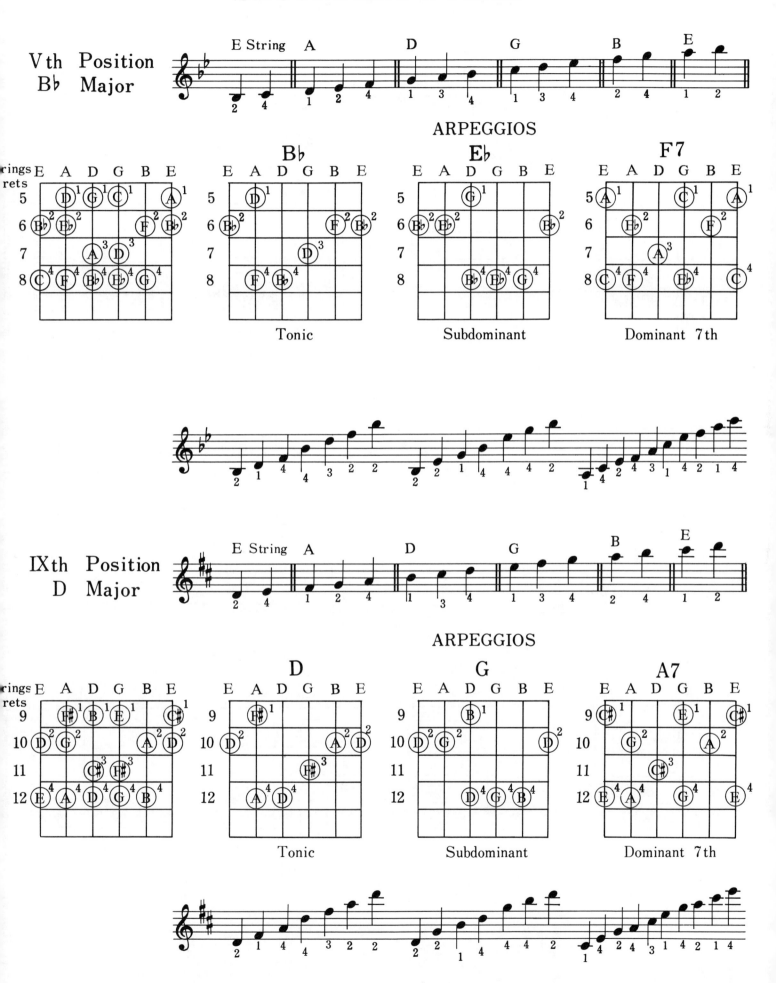

ARPEGGIOS

Bb — Tonic
Eb — Subdominant
F7 — Dominant 7th

D — Tonic
G — Subdominant
A7 — Dominant 7th

SECONDARY FORMS

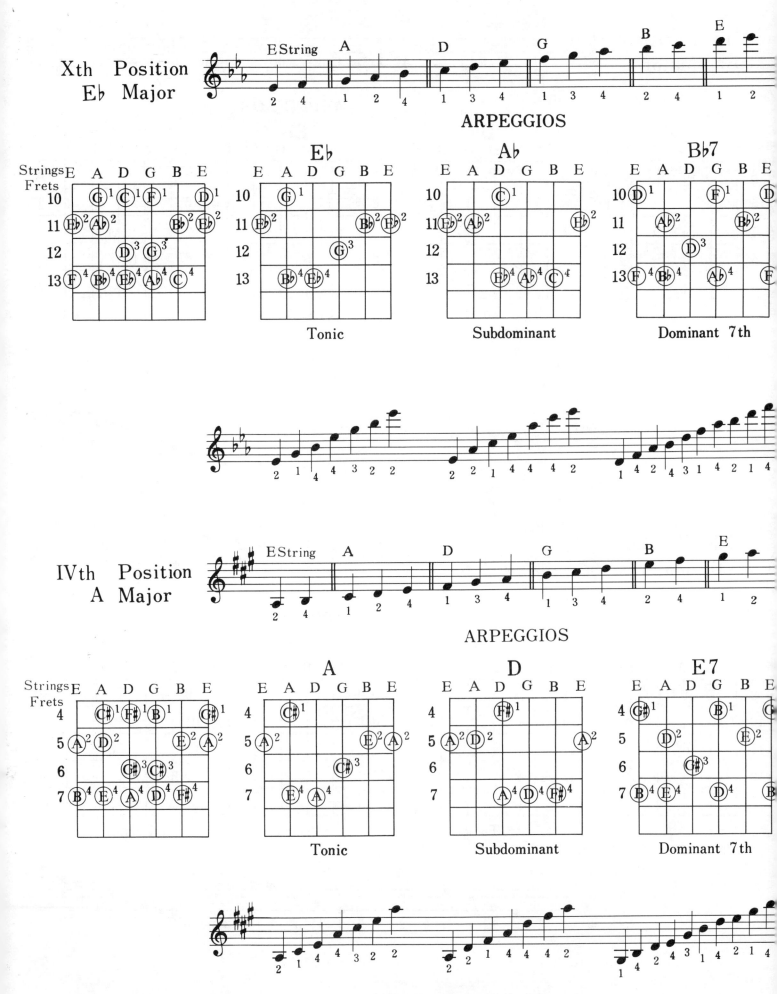

SECONDARY FORMS

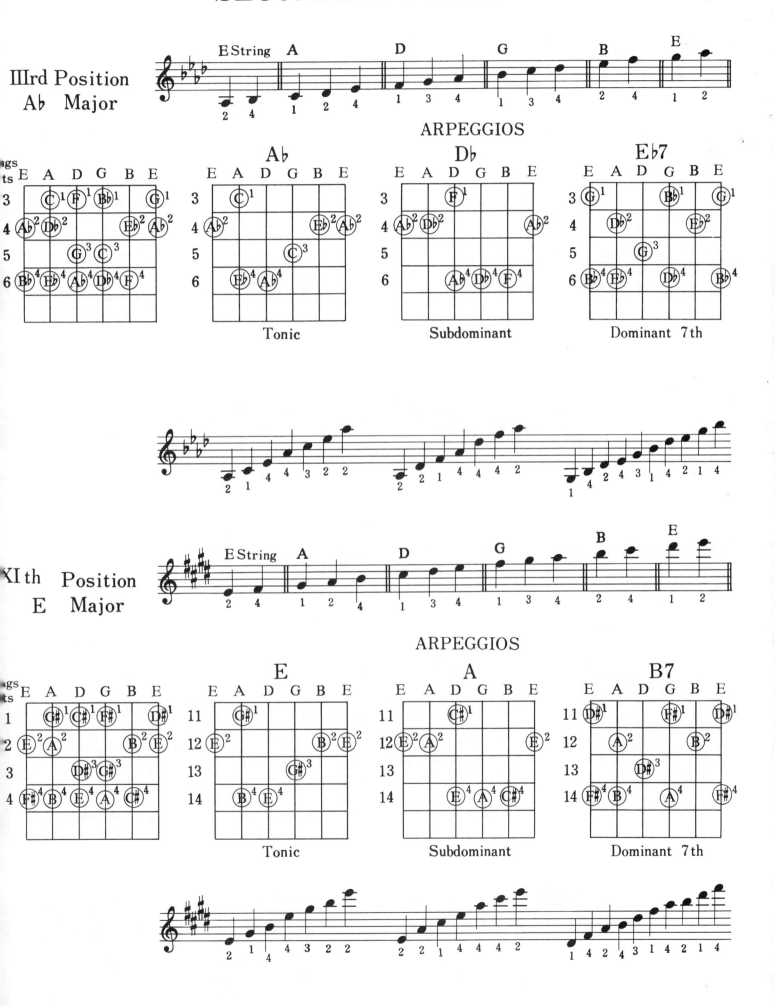

SECONDARY FORMS

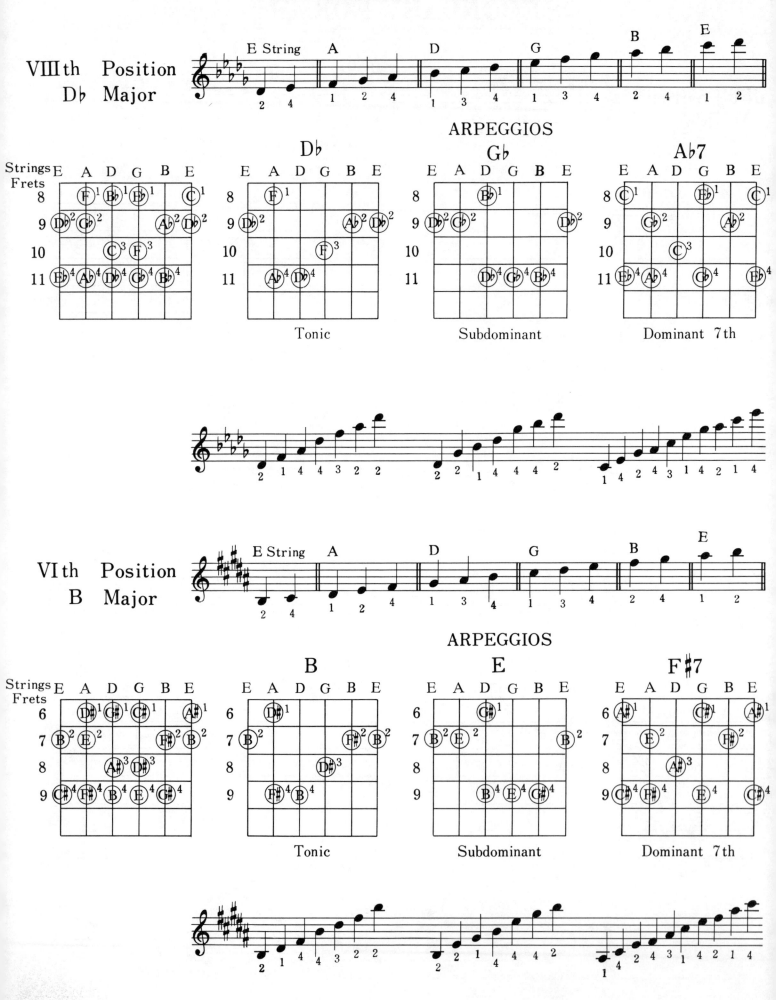

VIIIth Position
D♭ Major

ARPEGGIOS

D♭ — Tonic

G♭ — Subdominant

A♭7 — Dominant 7th

VIth Position
B Major

ARPEGGIOS

B — Tonic

E — Subdominant

F♯7 — Dominant 7th

SECONDARY FORMS

Ist Position Gb Major

ARPEGGIOS

Gb — Tonic

Cb — Subdominant

Db7 — Dominant 7th

These two keys are enharmonically equivalent.

Ist Position F# Major

ARPEGGIOS

F# — Tonic

B — Subdominant

C#7 — Dominant 7th

TERTIARY FORMS

C Major

Vth Position

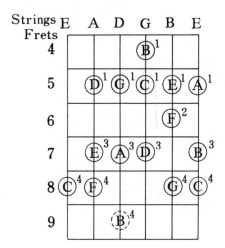

The extension to a fret beyond the normal position is called a <u>fifth fret stretch</u>.
Choice of fingering will depend on the particular playing situation.

ARPEGGIOS

C

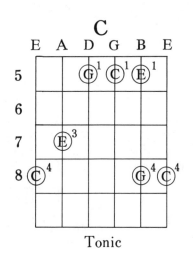

Tonic

F

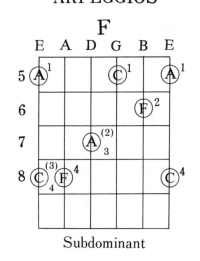

Subdominant

G7

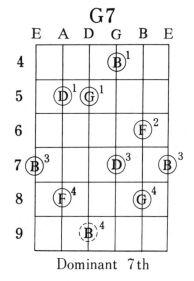

Dominant 7th

TERTIARY FORMS

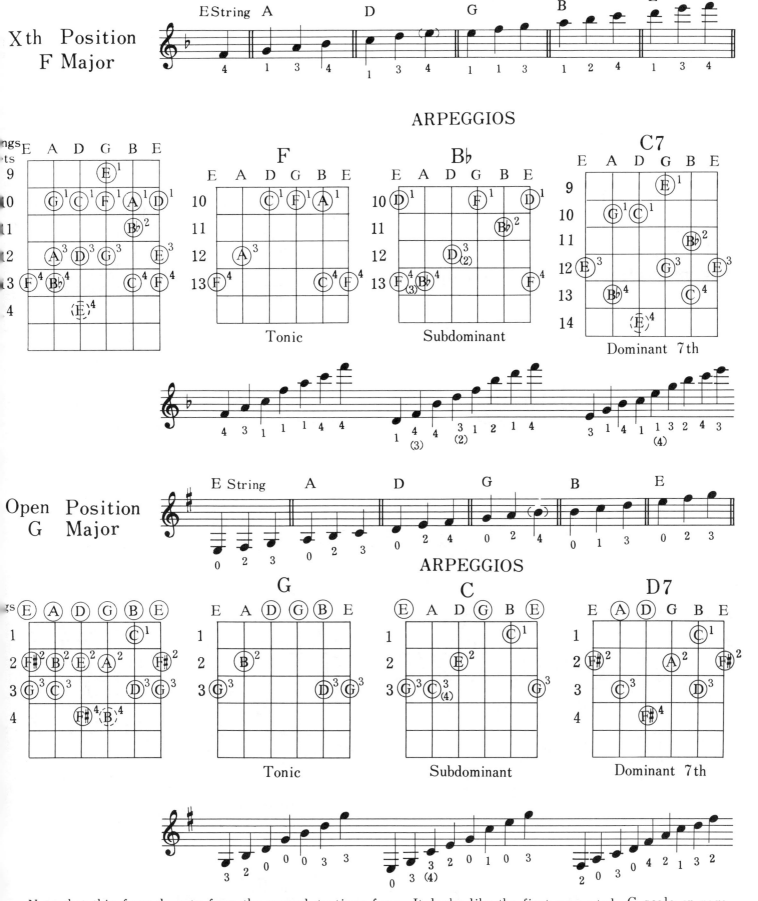

Note that this form departs from the normal tertiary form. It looks like the first presented C scale on page 10 with the exception of F♯ for F. The tertiary form for C is played precisely as other tertiary forms I octave higher in the 12th position. The lower scale is here presented because of its greater useability.

TERTIARY FORMS

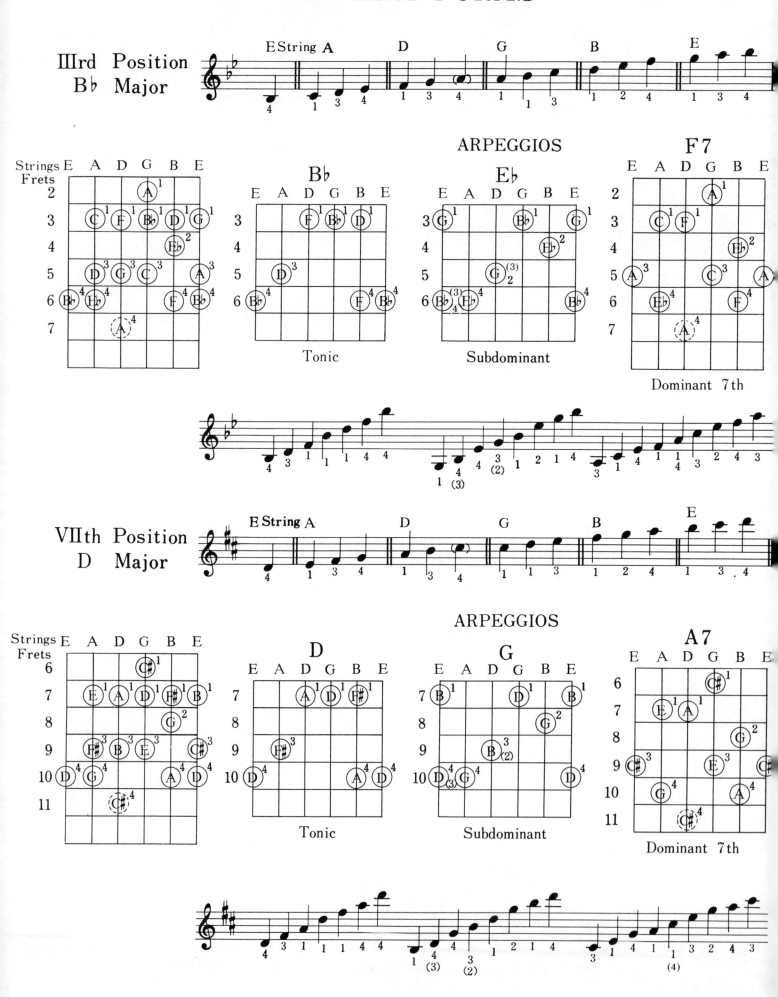

IIIrd Position
B♭ Major

ARPEGGIOS

B♭ — Tonic

E♭ — Subdominant

F 7 — Dominant 7th

VIIth Position
D Major

ARPEGGIOS

D — Tonic

G — Subdominant

A 7 — Dominant 7th

TERTIARY FORMS

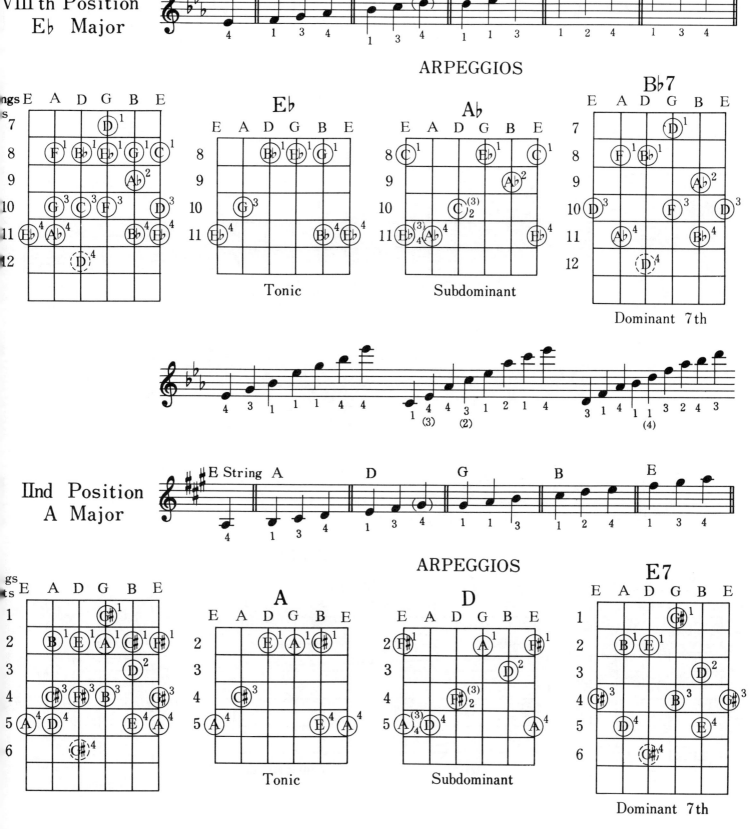

28

TERTIARY FORMS

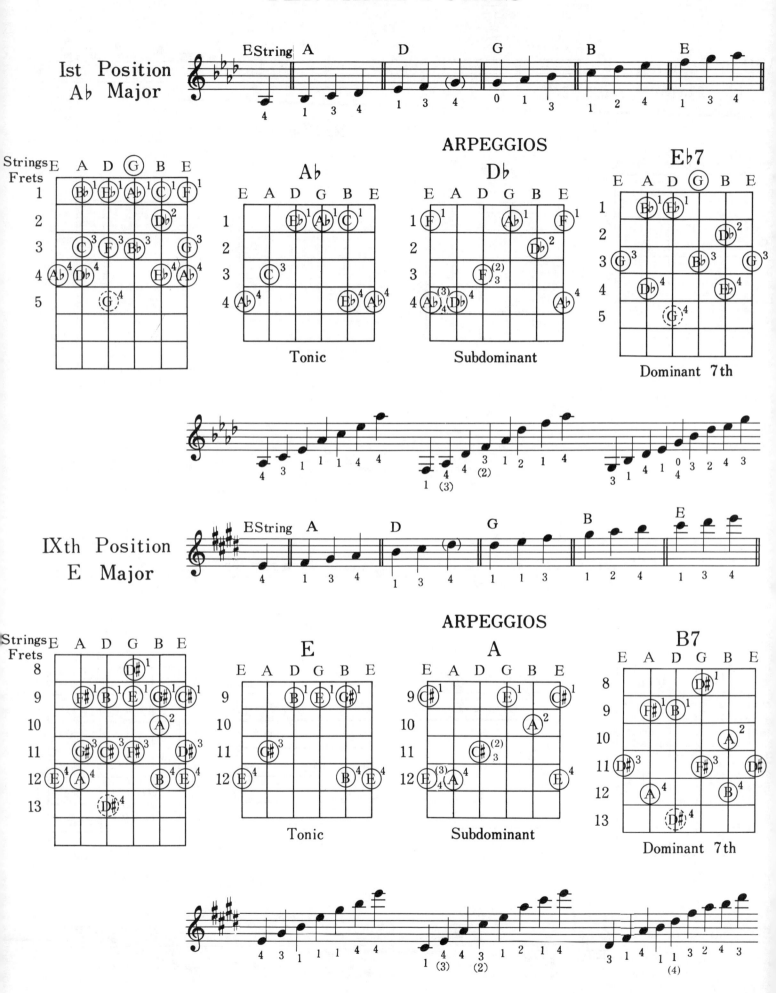

TERTIARY FORMS

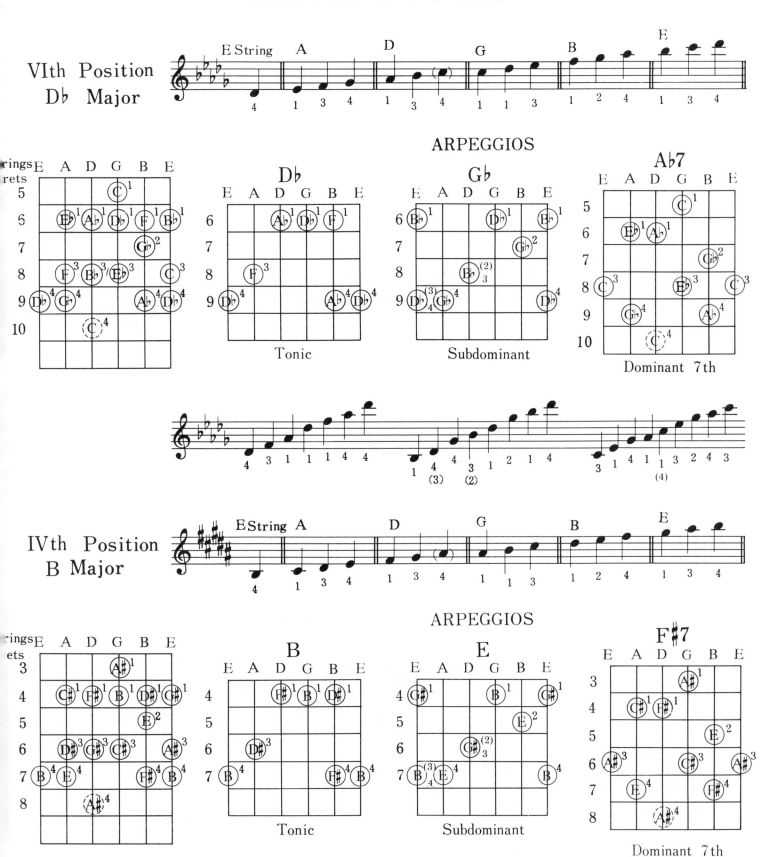

ARPEGGIOS

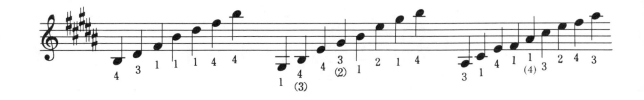

TERTIARY FORMS

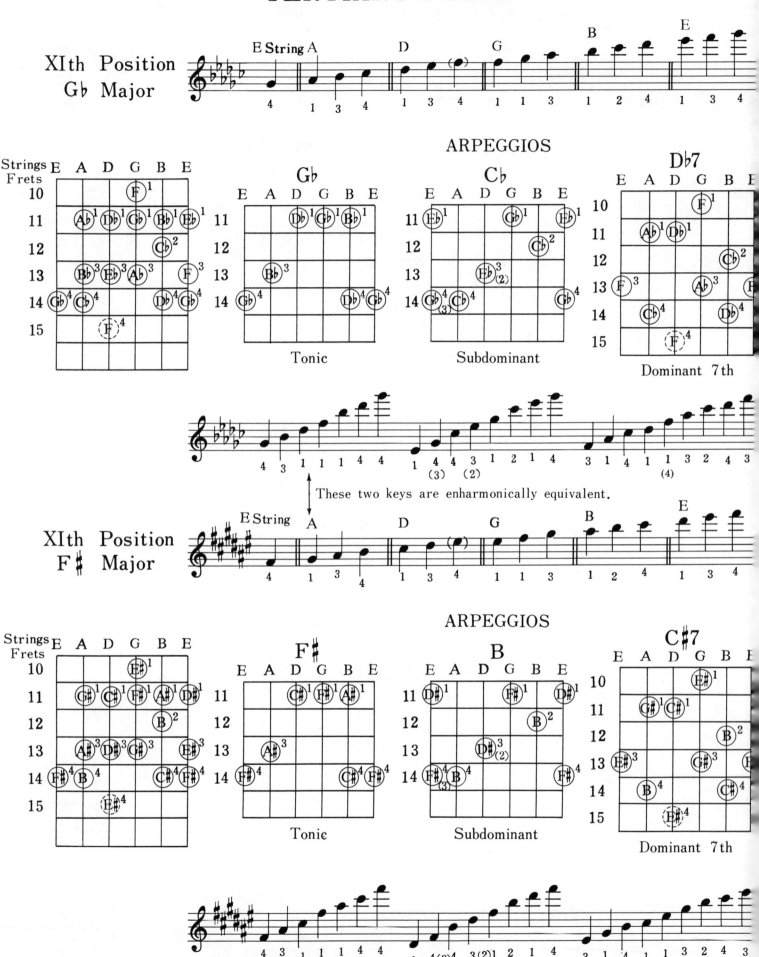

ARPEGGIOS

These two keys are enharmonically equivalent.

Gb — Tonic · Cb — Subdominant · Db7 — Dominant 7th

F# — Tonic · B — Subdominant · C#7 — Dominant 7th

30

QUATERNARY FORMS
C Major

IInd Position

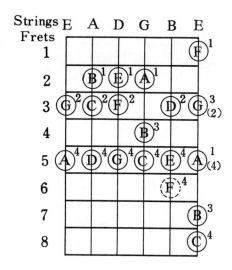

ARPEGGIOS

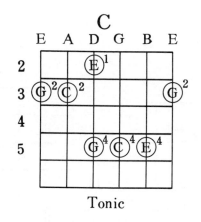

Tonic

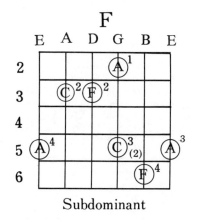

Subdominant

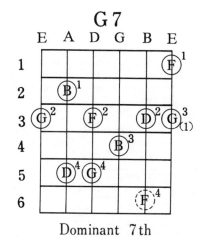

Dominant 7th

QUATERNARY FORMS

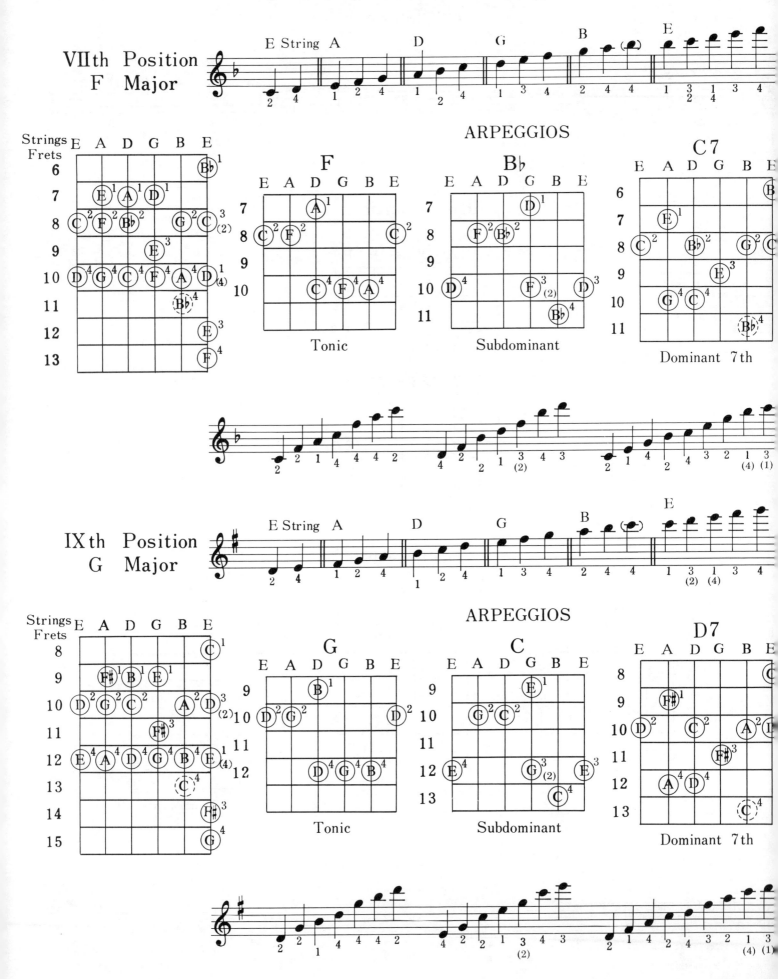

QUATERNARY FORMS

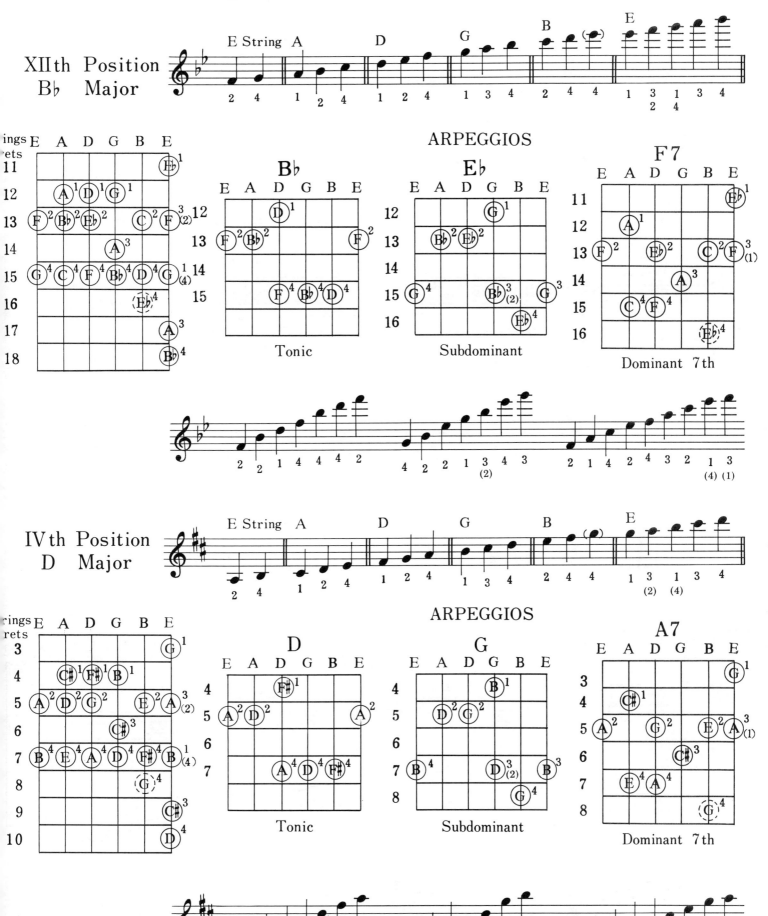

QUATERNARY FORMS

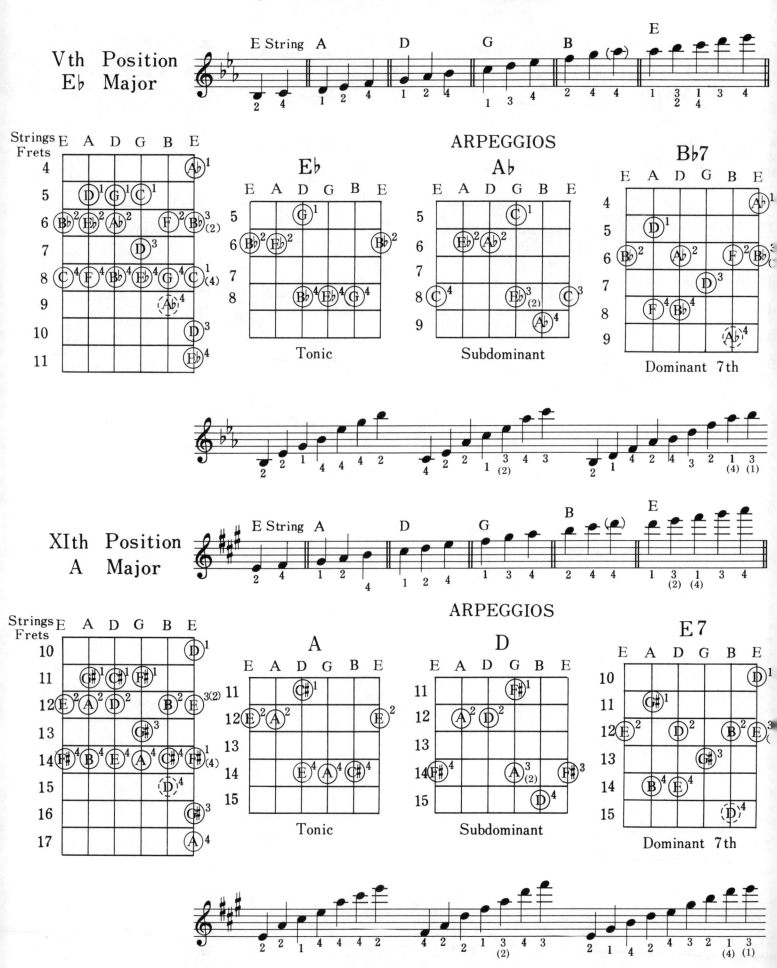

QUATERNARY FORMS

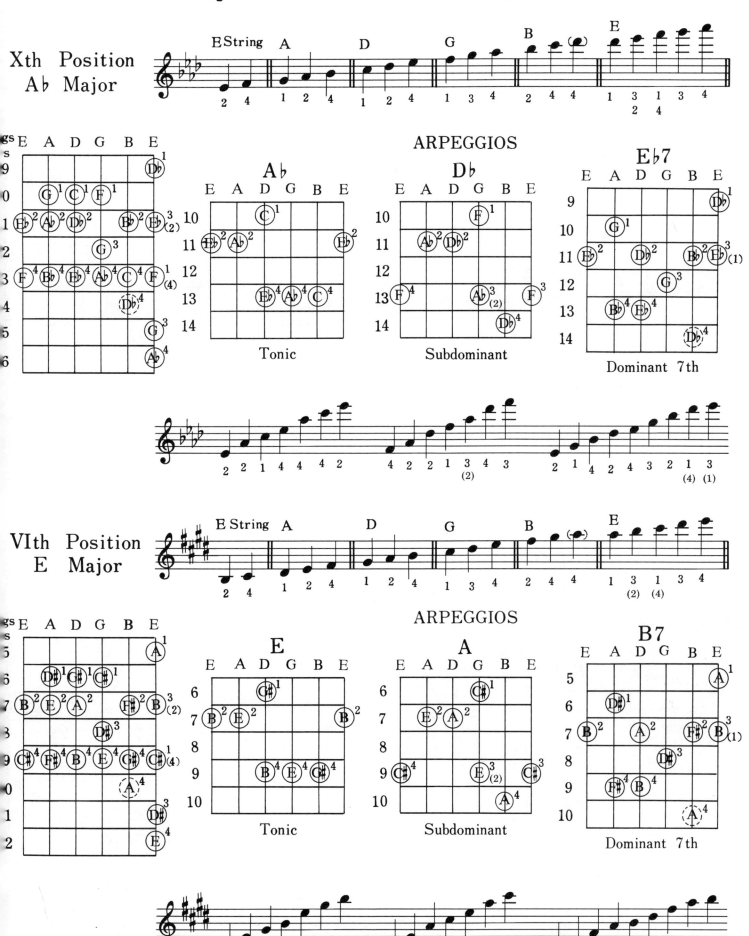

QUATERNARY FORMS

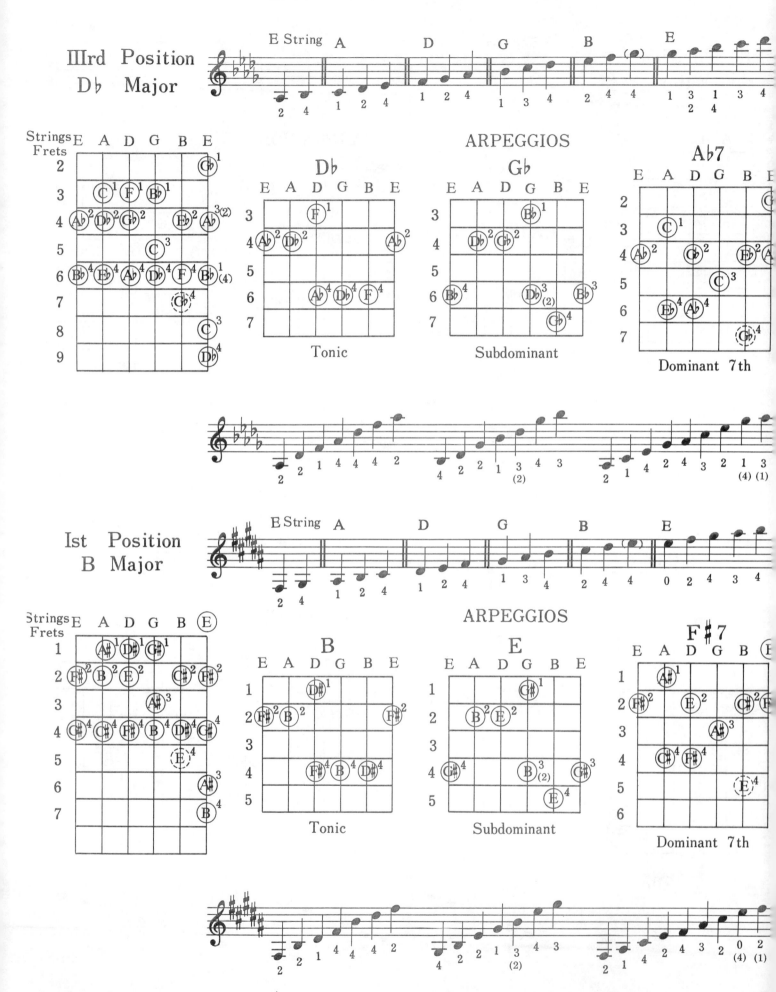

QUATERNARY FORMS

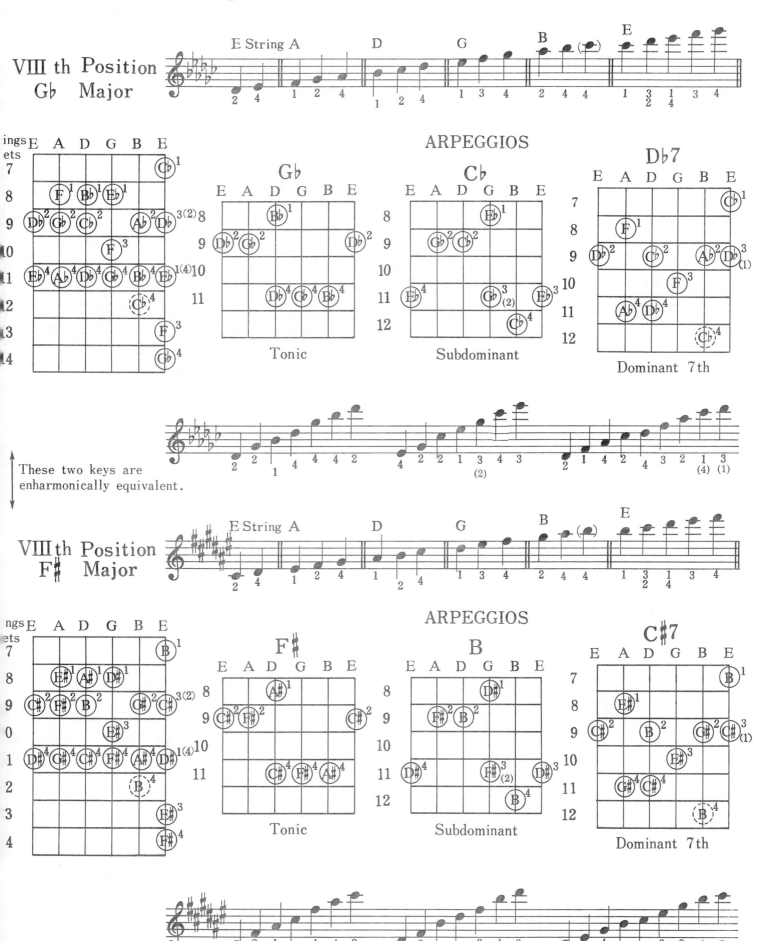

These two keys are enharmonically equivalent.

PART TWO - MINOR FORMS

Next, consider the minor forms-scales and arpeggios. Each major key has a relative minor key, found o
minor third below the major key. Minor keys have the same key signature (sharps or flats) as the relative ma;
key. For example, the relative   minor of C major is A minor. The relative minor of F major is D minor.

PRIMARY FORMS
Open Position - A Minor

NATURAL FORM

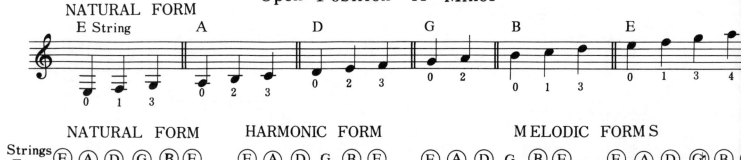

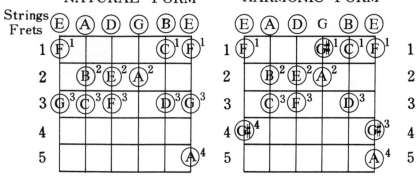

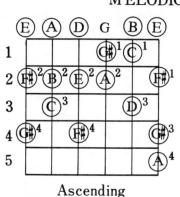

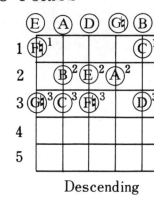

Ascending   Descending

HARMONIC FORM · 7th step is raised in both directions.

MELODIC FORM - 6th and 7th steps are raised ascending

6th and 7th steps are natural descending

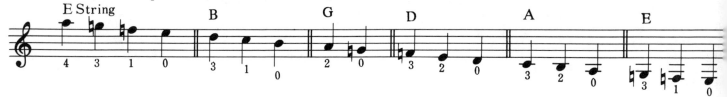

ARPEGGIOS

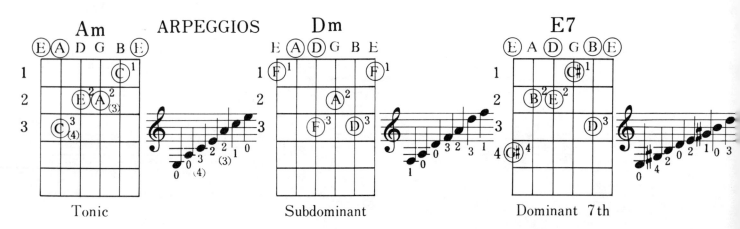

Am   Dm   E7

Tonic   Subdominant   Dominant 7th

PRIMARY FORMS

Vth Position   D Minor-Harmonic

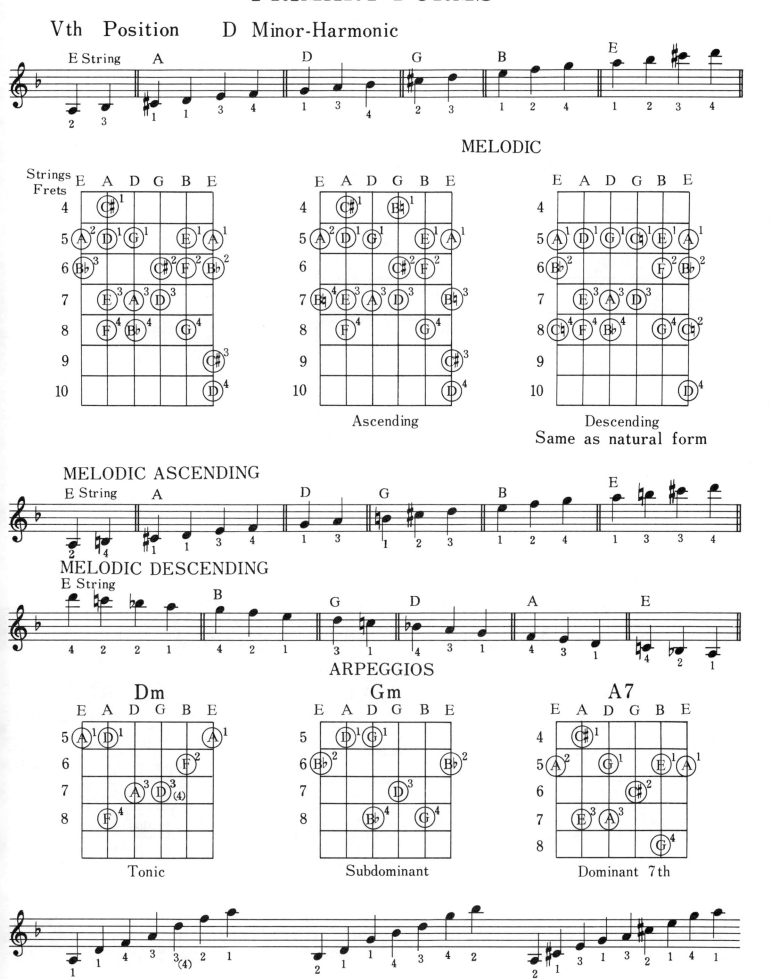

MELODIC

Ascending

Descending
Same as natural form

MELODIC ASCENDING

MELODIC DESCENDING

ARPEGGIOS

Dm — Tonic

Gm — Subdominant

A7 — Dominant 7th

PRIMARY FORMS

VIIth Position   E Minor-Harmonic

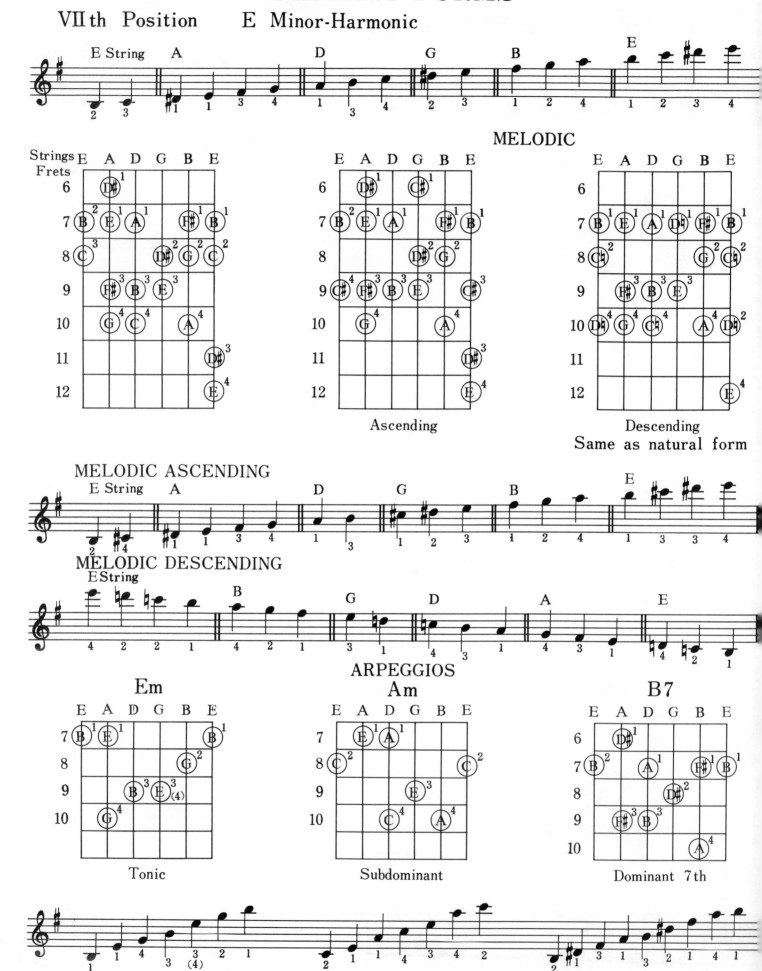

PRIMARY FORMS

Xth Position   G Minor-Harmonic

MELODIC

MELODIC ASCENDING

MELODIC DESCENDING

ARPEGGIOS

Gm   Cm   D7

Tonic   Subdominant   Dominant 7th

PRIMARY FORMS

IInd Position   B Minor-Harmonic

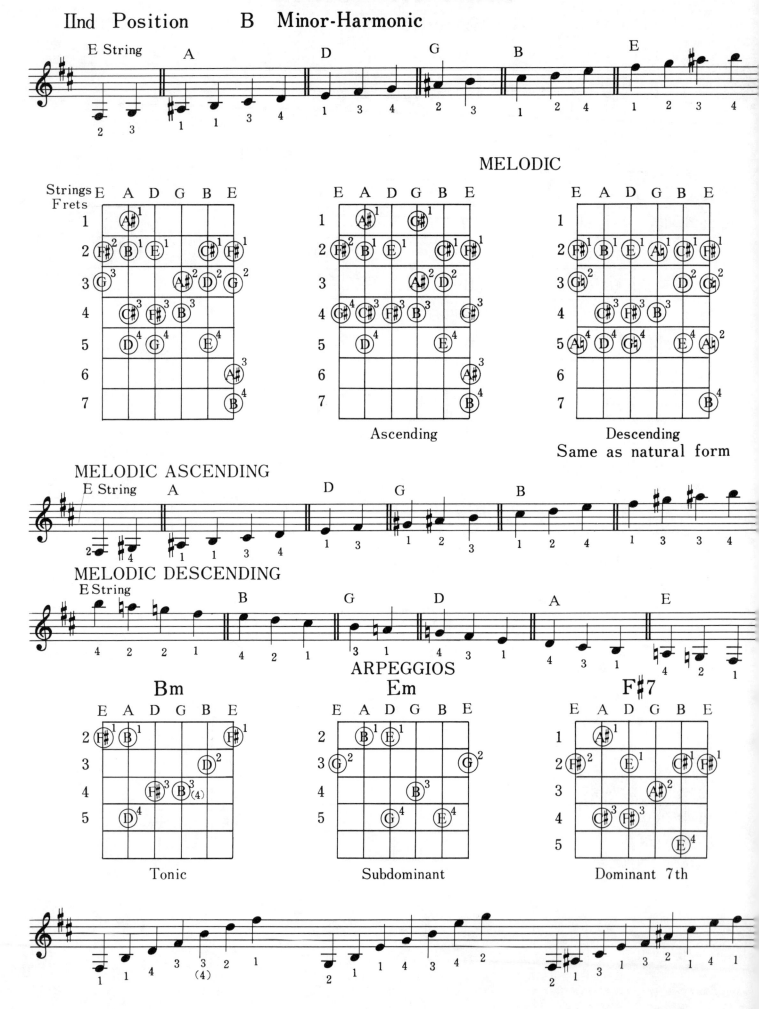

MELODIC

Ascending

Descending
Same as natural form

MELODIC ASCENDING

MELODIC DESCENDING

ARPEGGIOS

Bm   Em   F#7

Tonic   Subdominant   Dominant 7th

PRIMARY FORMS

IIIrd Position   C Minor-Harmonic

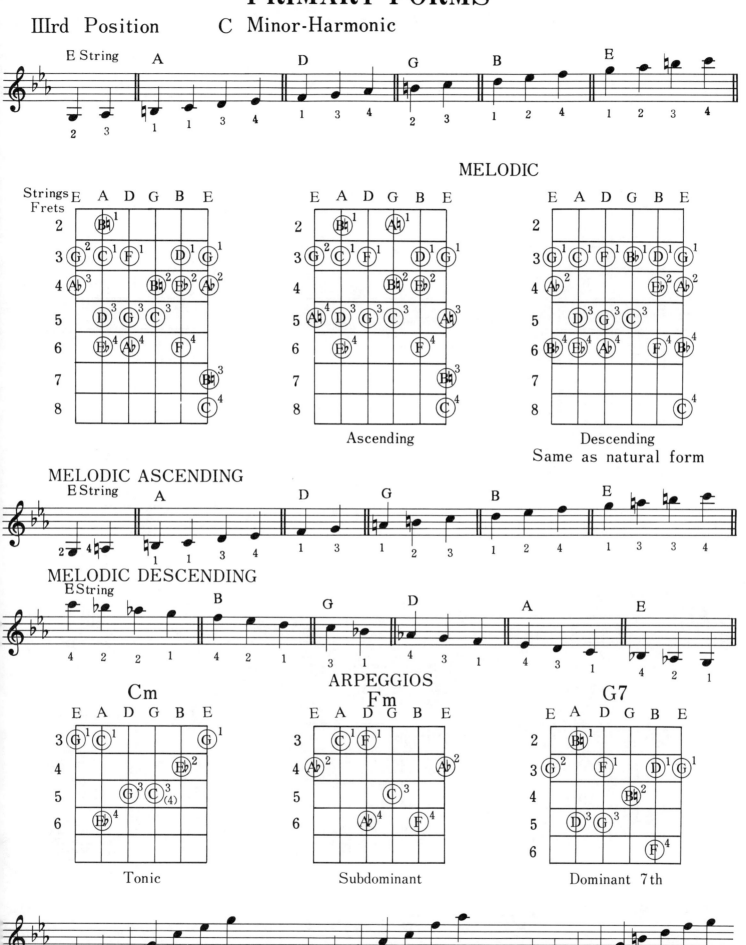

MELODIC

Ascending

Descending
Same as natural form

MELODIC ASCENDING

MELODIC DESCENDING

ARPEGGIOS

Cm

Fm

G7

Tonic

Subdominant

Dominant 7th

PRIMARY FORMS

PRIMARY FORMS

VIIIth Position   F Minor-Harmonic

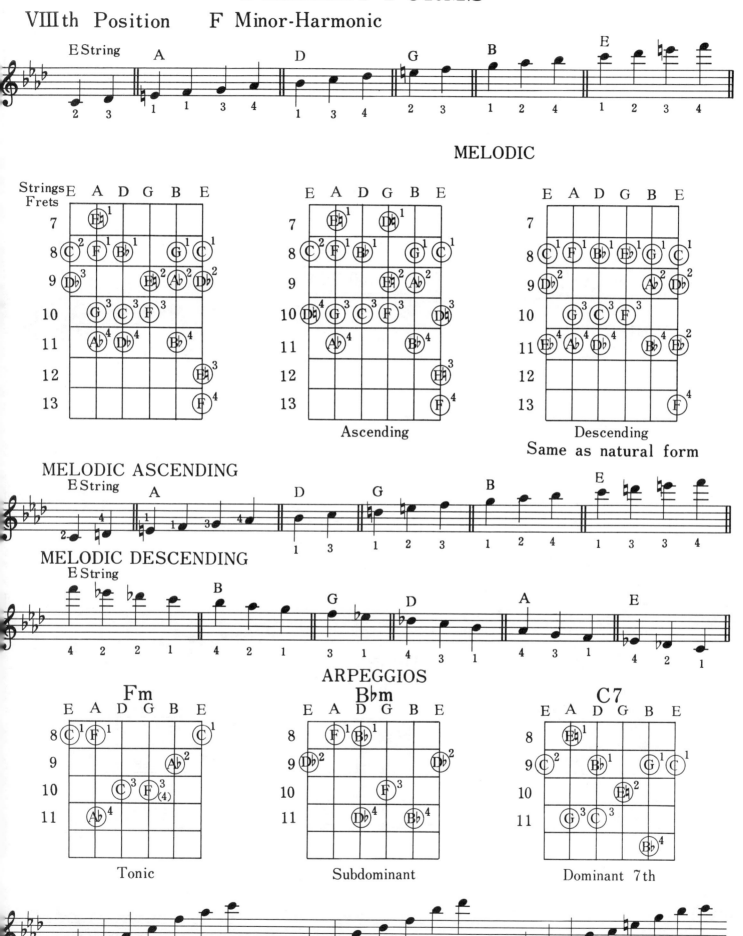

MELODIC

Ascending

Descending
Same as natural form

MELODIC ASCENDING

MELODIC DESCENDING

ARPEGGIOS

Fm

Bbm

C7

Tonic

Subdominant

Dominant 7th

PRIMARY FORMS

IVth Position   C♯ Minor-Harmonic

MELODIC

MELODIC ASCENDING

MELODIC DESCENDING

ARPEGGIOS

Tonic   Subdominant   Dominant 7th

Ascending

Descending
Same as natural form

PRIMARY FORMS

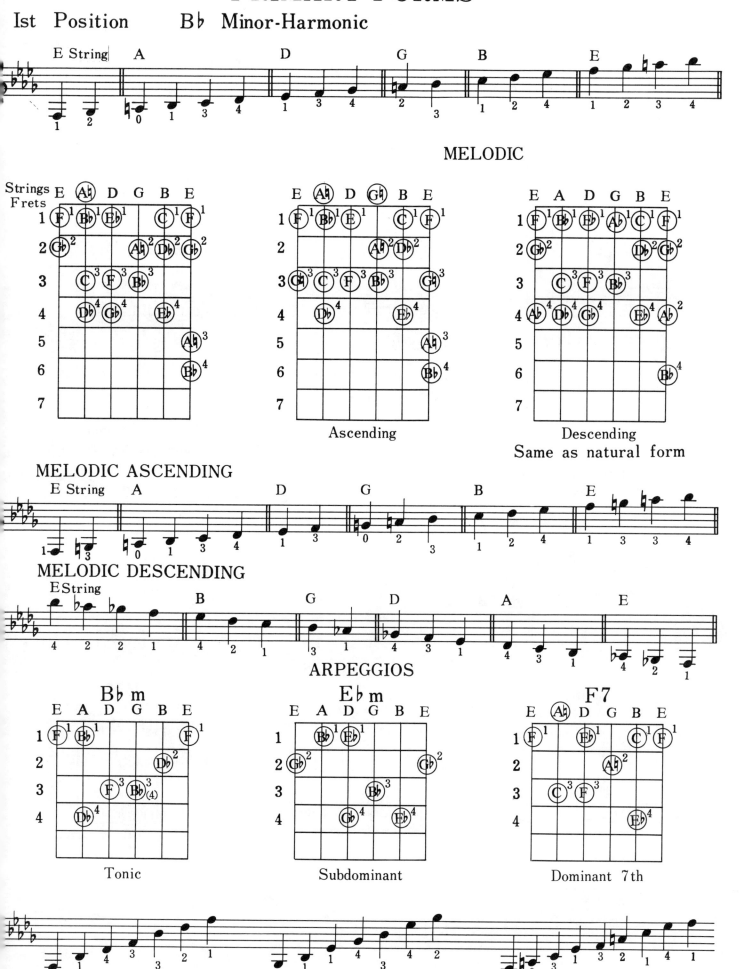

PRIMARY FORMS

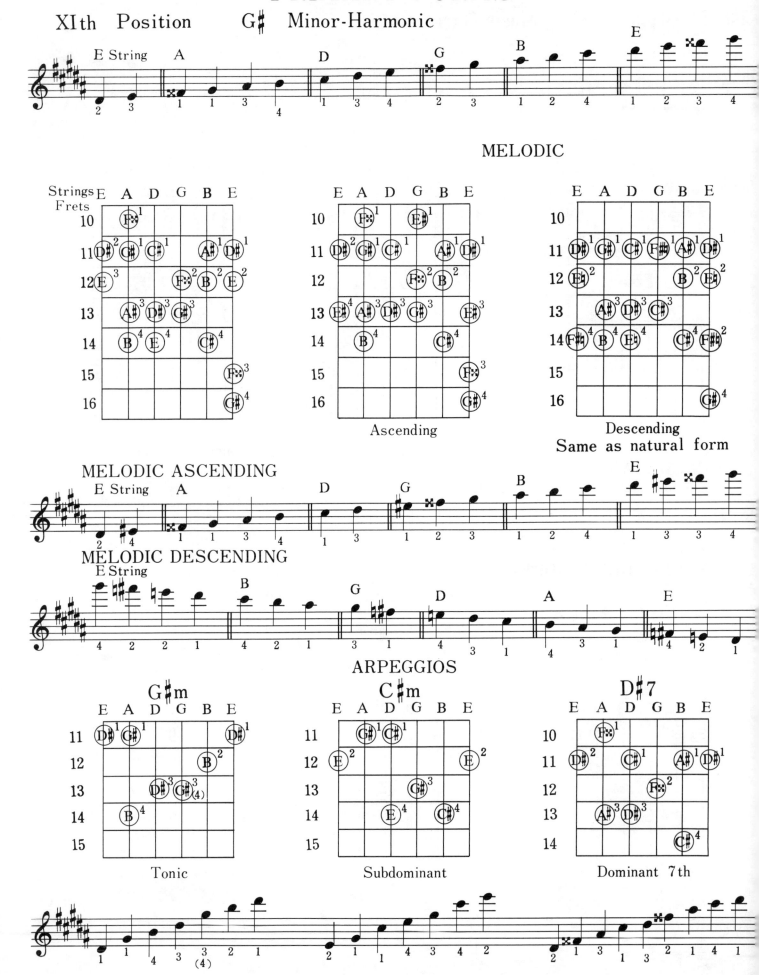

PRIMARY FORMS

VIth Position E♭ Minor-Harmonic

This key is enharmonically equivalent to D♯ Minor(p 50)

MELODIC

MELODIC ASCENDING

MELODIC DESCENDING

Ascending

Descending
Same as natural form

ARPEGGIOS

Tonic

Subdominant

Dominant 7th

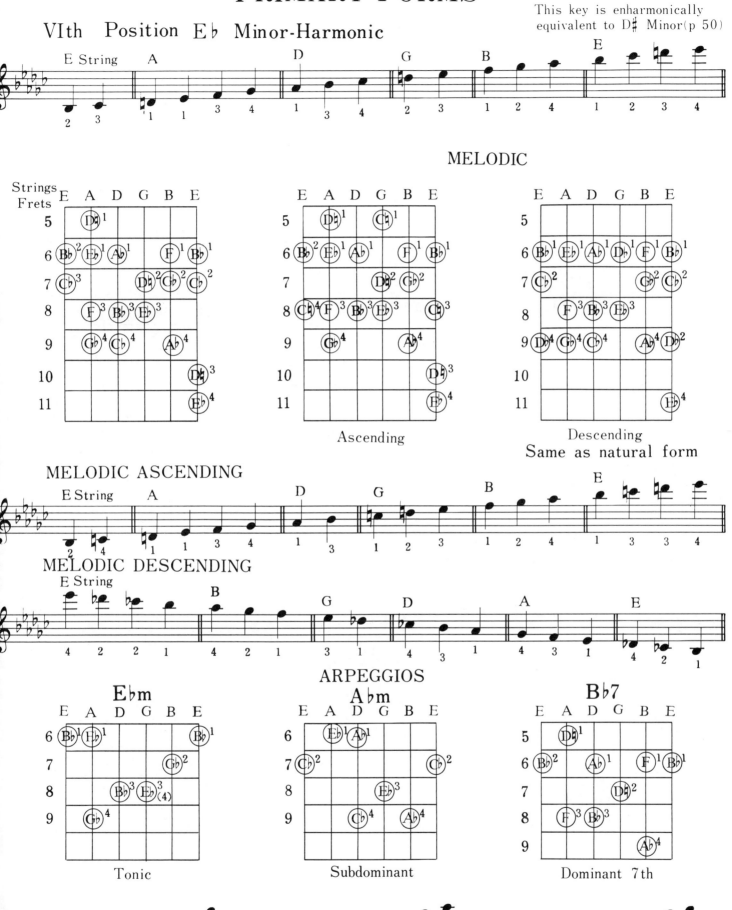

PRIMARY FORMS

This key is enharmonically
equivalent to Eb Minor (p 49)

VIth Position   D# Minor-Harmonic

MELODIC

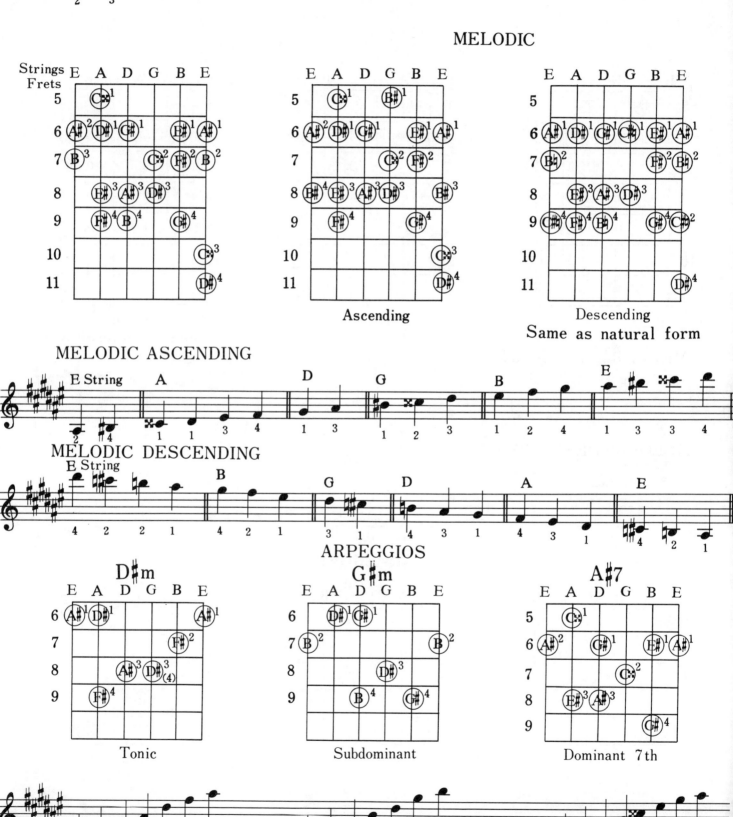

Ascending

Descending

Same as natural form

MELODIC ASCENDING

MELODIC DESCENDING

ARPEGGIOS

D#m — Tonic

G#m — Subdominant

A#7 — Dominant 7th

SECONDARY FORMS

VIIth Position   A Minor-Harmonic

MELODIC

Ascending

Descending

Same as natural form

MELODIC ASCENDING

MELODIC DESCENDING

ARPEGGIOS

Am — Tonic

Dm — Subdominant

E7 — Dominant 7th

SECONDARY FORMS

XIIth Position D Minor-Harmonic

MELODIC

Ascending

Descending
Same as natural form

MELODIC ASCENDING

MELODIC DESCENDING

ARPEGGIOS

Dm
Tonic

Gm
Subdominant

A7
Dominant 7th

SECONDARY FORMS

IInd Position   E Minor-Harmonic

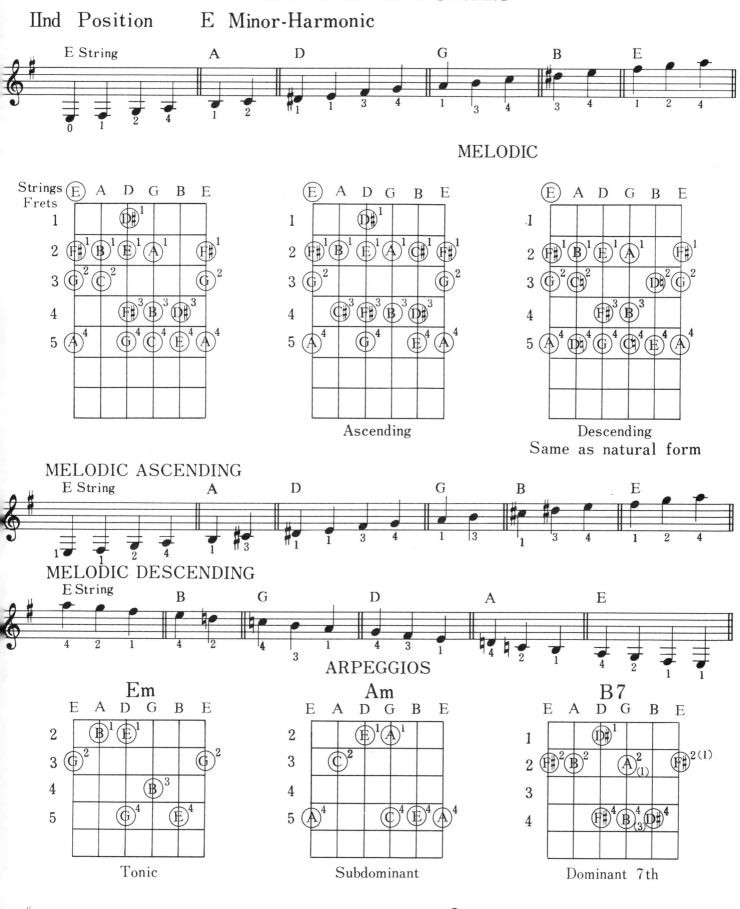

MELODIC

MELODIC ASCENDING

MELODIC DESCENDING

ARPEGGIOS

Em — Tonic

Am — Subdominant

B7 — Dominant 7th

SECONDARY FORMS

Vth Position   G   Minor-Harmonic

MELODIC

Ascending

Descending
Same as natural form

MELODIC ASCENDING

MELODIC DESCENDING

ARPEGGIOS

Gm

Cm

D7

Tonic

Subdominant

Dominant 7th

SECONDARY FORMS

SECONDARY FORMS

Xth Position   C Minor-Harmonic

MELODIC

Ascending

Descending

Same as natural form

MELODIC ASCENDING

MELODIC DESCENDING

ARPEGGIOS

Cm

Tonic

Fm

Subdominant

G7

Dominant 7th

SECONDARY FORMS

IVth Position   F♯ Minor-Harmonic

MELODIC

Ascending

Descending
Same as natural form

MELODIC ASCENDING

MELODIC DESCENDING

ARPEGGIOS

F♯m — Tonic

Bm — Subdominant

C♯7 — Dominant 7th

58

SECONDARY FORMS

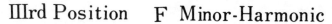

SECONDARY FORMS

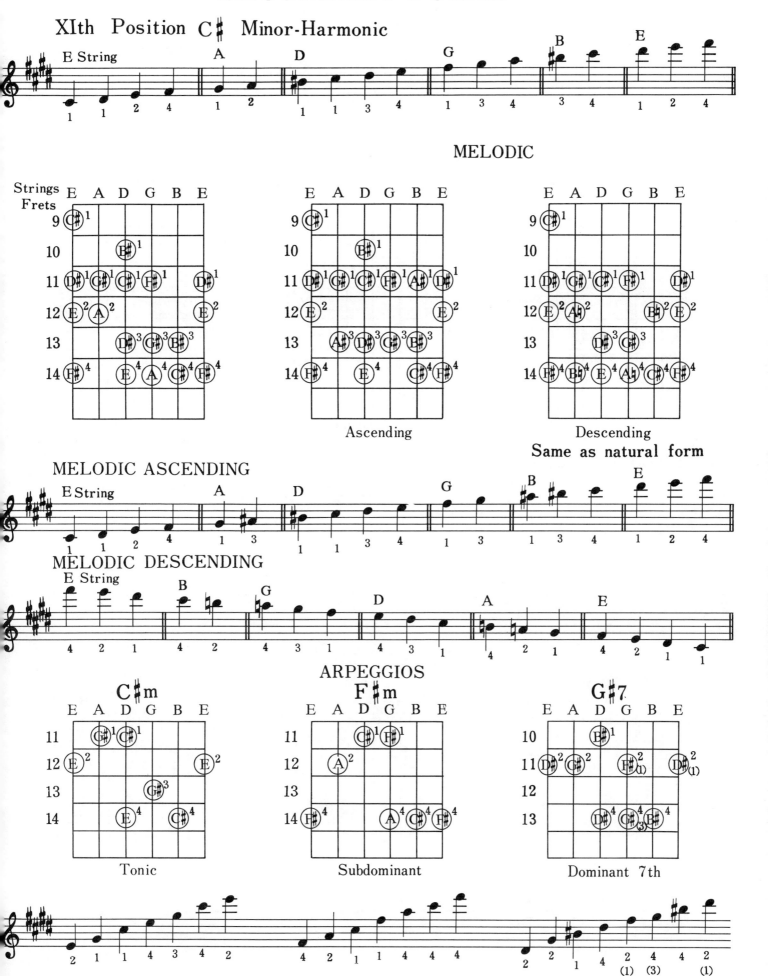

SECONDARY FORMS

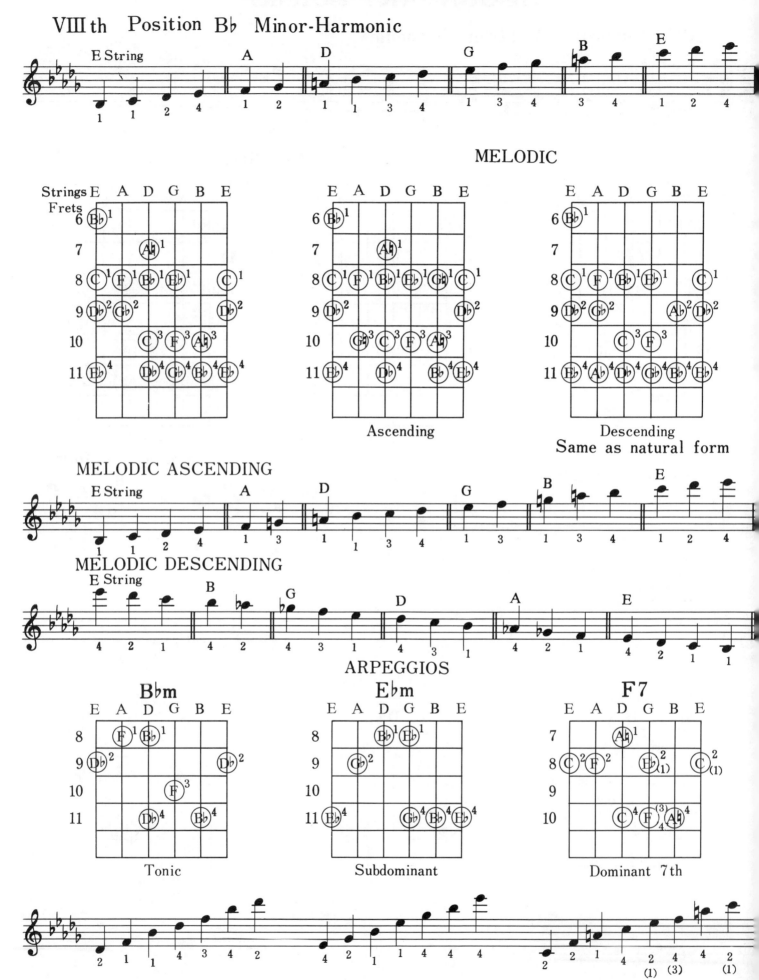

VIIIth Position Bb Minor-Harmonic

MELODIC

MELODIC ASCENDING

MELODIC DESCENDING

ARPEGGIOS

Bbm — Tonic

Ebm — Subdominant

F7 — Dominant 7th

SECONDARY FORMS

VIth Position   G♯ Minor - Harmonic

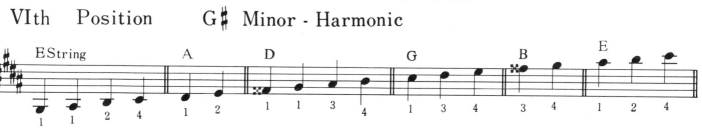

MELODIC

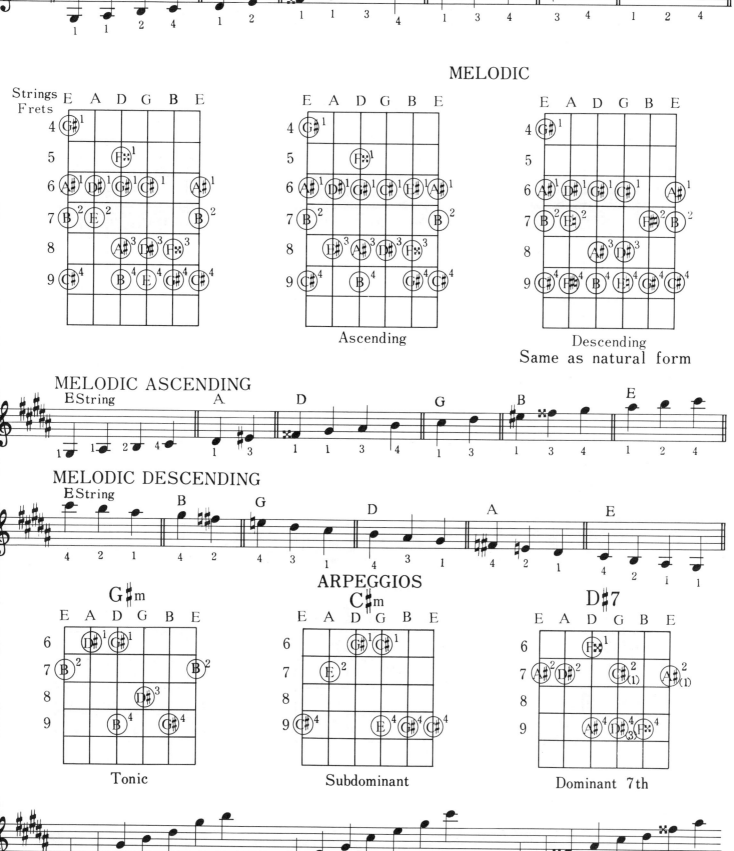

Ascending

Descending
Same as natural form

MELODIC ASCENDING

MELODIC DESCENDING

ARPEGGIOS

G♯m — Tonic

C♯m — Subdominant

D♯7 — Dominant 7th

SECONDARY FORMS

SECONDARY FORMS

Ist Position D♯ Minor-Harmonic

This key is enharmonically equivalent to E♭ minor (p. 62)

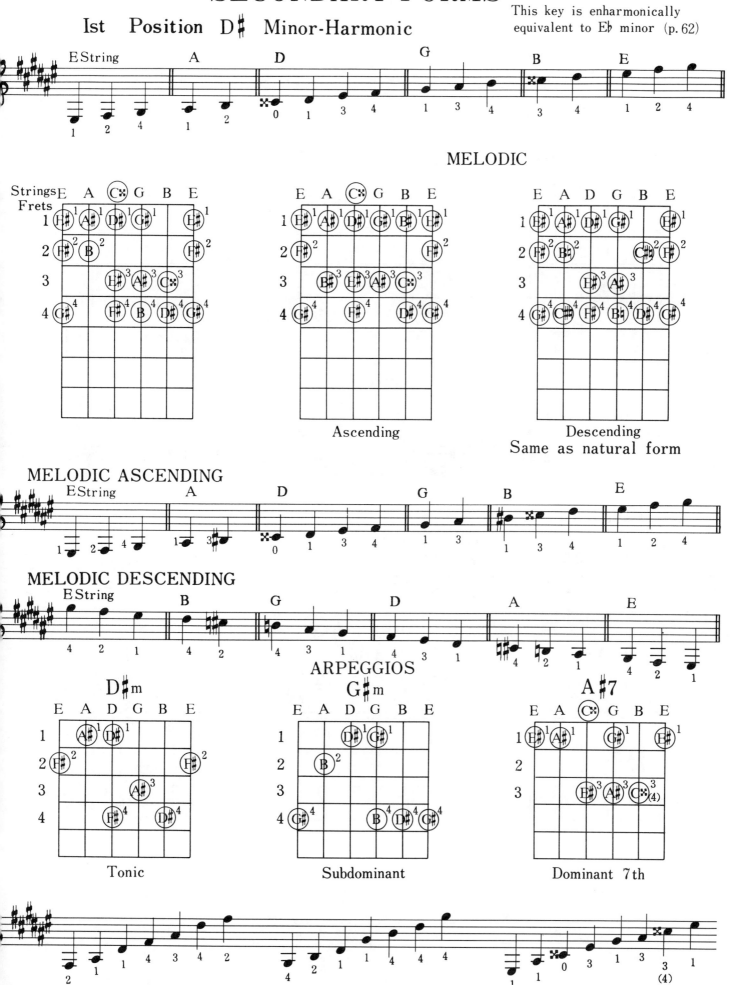

MELODIC

Ascending

Descending
Same as natural form

MELODIC ASCENDING

MELODIC DESCENDING

ARPEGGIOS

D♯m   G♯m   A♯7

Tonic   Subdominant   Dominant 7th

TERTIARY FORMS

Vth Position   A Minor-Harmonic

MELODIC

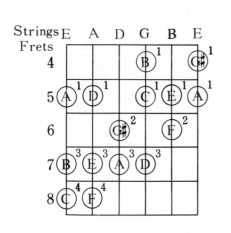
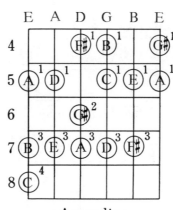
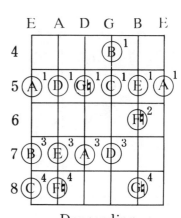

Ascending   Descending

Same as natural form

MELODIC ASCENDING

MELODIC DESCENDING

ARPEGGIOS

Am   Dm   E7

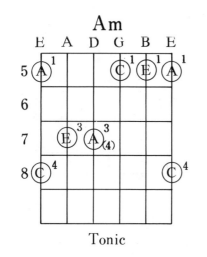
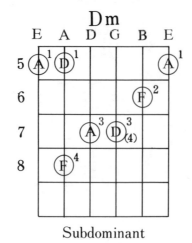
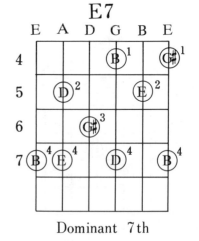

Tonic   Subdominant   Dominant 7th

TERTIARY FORMS

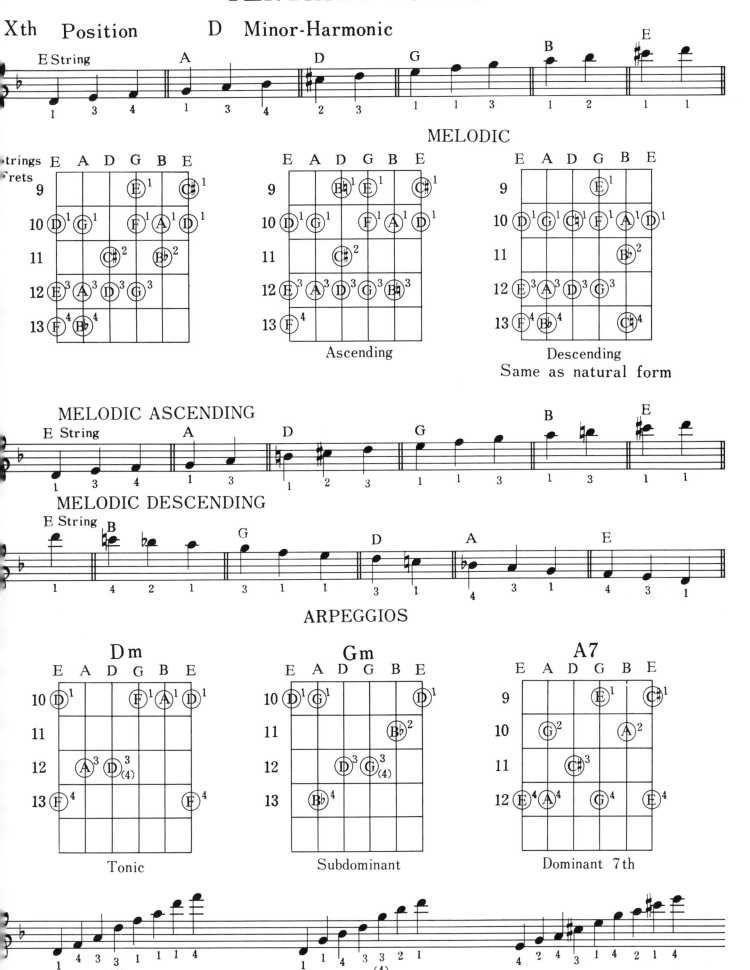

Xth Position   D Minor-Harmonic

MELODIC

Ascending

Descending
Same as natural form

MELODIC ASCENDING

MELODIC DESCENDING

ARPEGGIOS

Dm

Gm

A7

Tonic

Subdominant

Dominant 7th

TERTIARY FORMS

This form departs from the normal tertiary form because it is played in the open position.
The tertiary form for E minor is played exactly the same as other tertiary forms 1
octave higher in the 12th position.

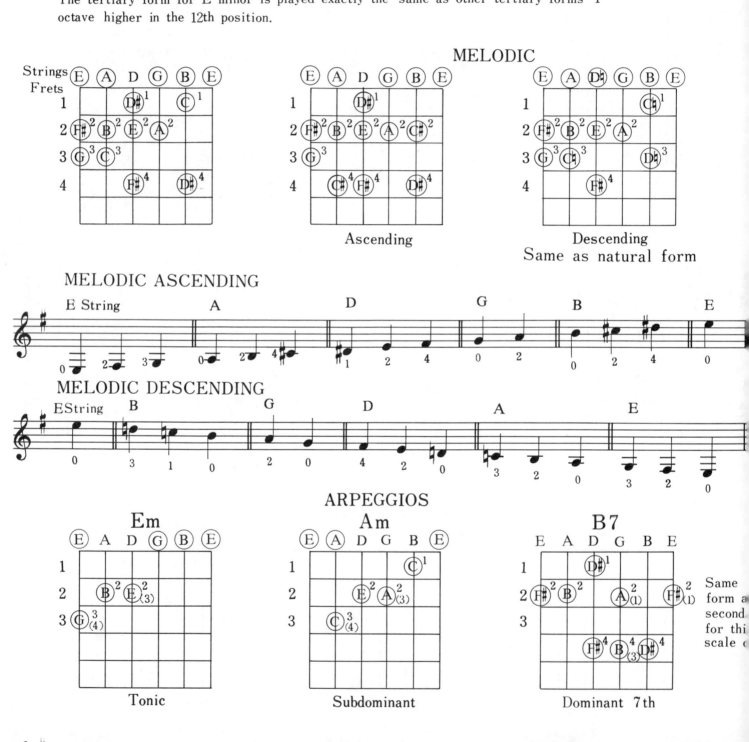

TERTIARY FORMS

IIIrd Position   G Minor-Harmonic

MELODIC

MELODIC ASCENDING

MELODIC DESCENDING

ARPEGGIOS

Gm — Tonic

Cm — Subdominant

D7 — Dominant 7th

TERTIARY FORMS

VIIth Position   **B Minor-Harmonic**

MELODIC

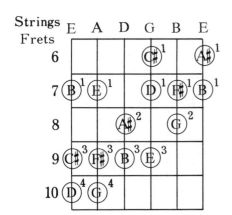 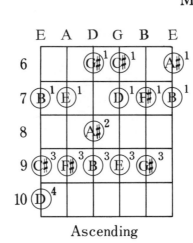 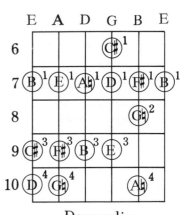

Ascending

Descending
Same as natural form

MELODIC ASCENDING

MELODIC DESCENDING

ARPEGGIOS

Bm   **Em**   **F#7**

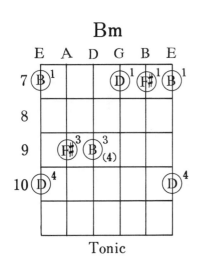 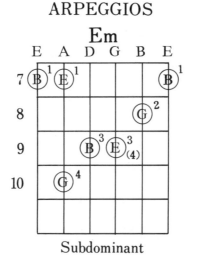 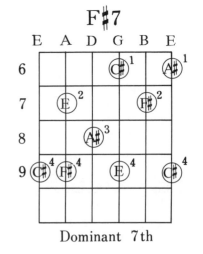

Tonic   Subdominant   Dominant 7th

TERTIARY FORMS

TERTIARY FORMS

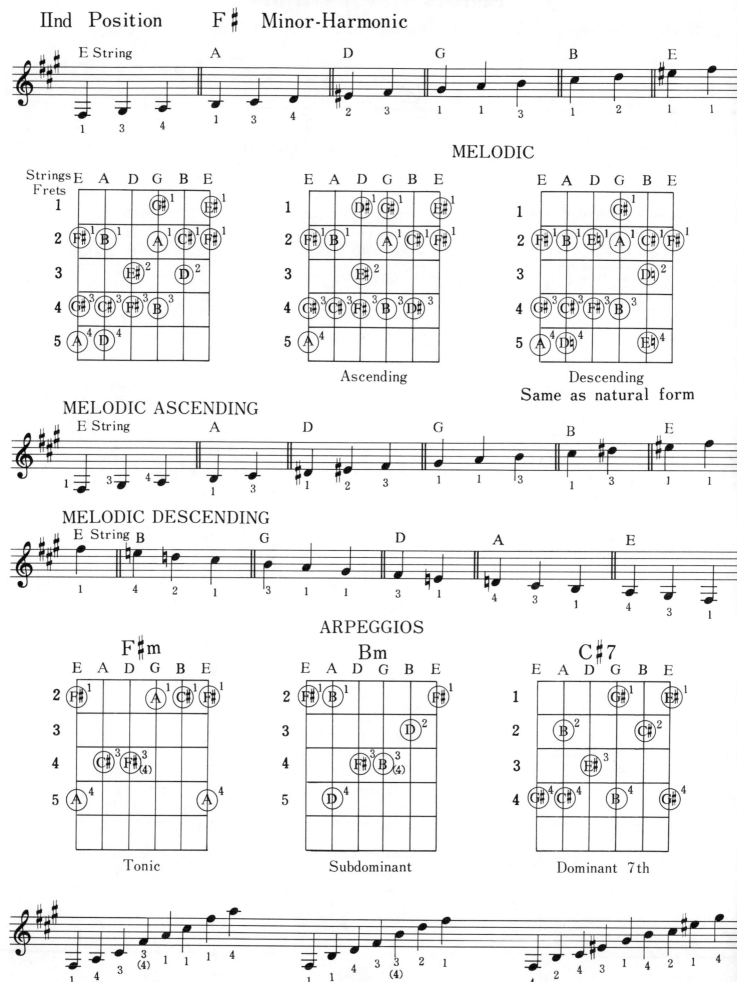

IInd Position   F♯ Minor-Harmonic

MELODIC

MELODIC ASCENDING

MELODIC DESCENDING

ARPEGGIOS

Tonic   Subdominant   Dominant 7th

TERTIARY FORMS

Ist Position *F Minor-Harmonic

MELODIC

Ascending

Descending
Same as natural form

MELODIC ASCENDING

MELODIC DESCENDING

ARPEGGIOS

Fm

Bbm

C 7

* Note fingering different for this key only.

Tonic

Subdominant

Dominant 7th

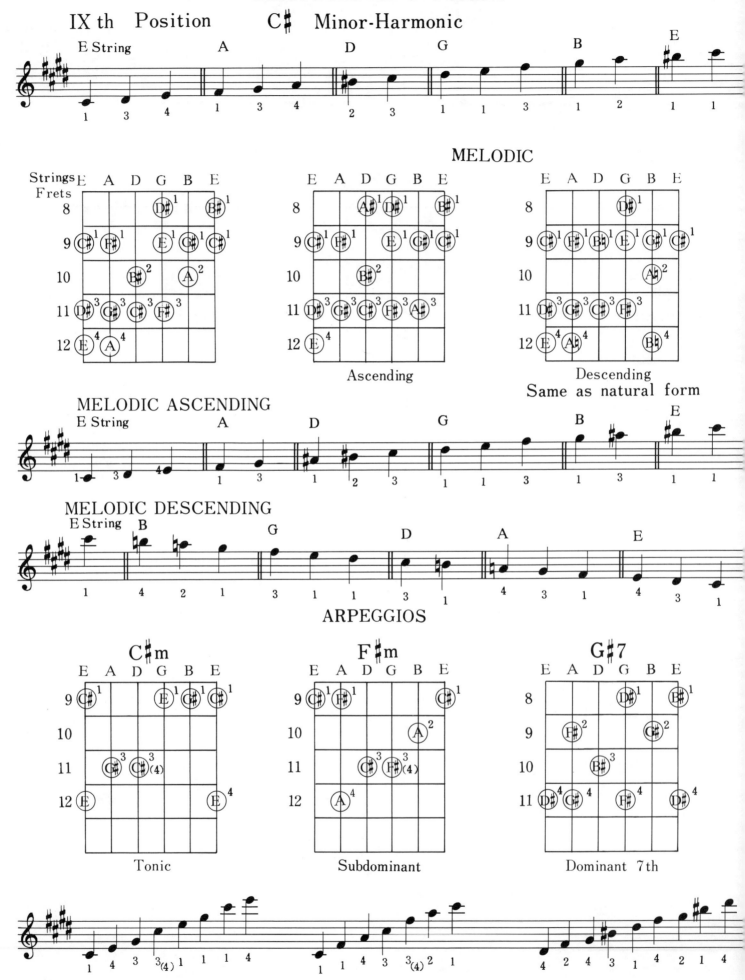

TERTIARY FORMS

TERTIARY FORMS

VI th Position   B♭ Minor-Harmonic

MELODIC

MELODIC ASCENDING

MELODIC DESCENDING

ARPEGGIOS

Tonic   Subdominant   Dominant 7th

TERTIARY FORMS

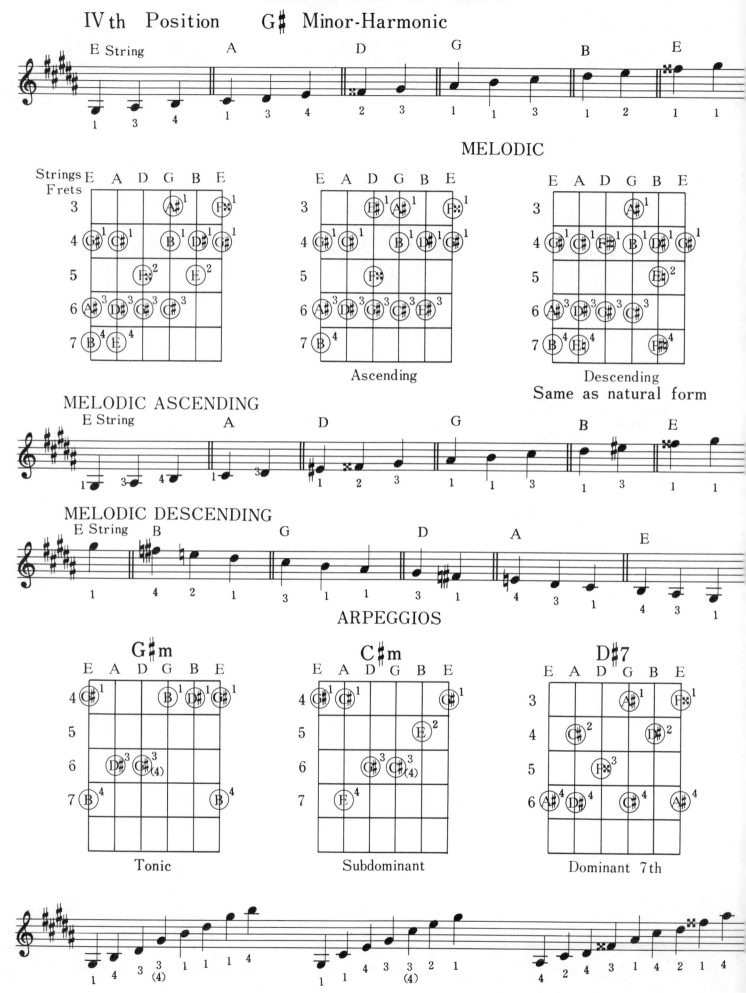

TERTIARY FORMS

XIth Position E♭ Minor-Harmonic

This key is enharmonically equivalent to D♯ minor (p 76)

MELODIC

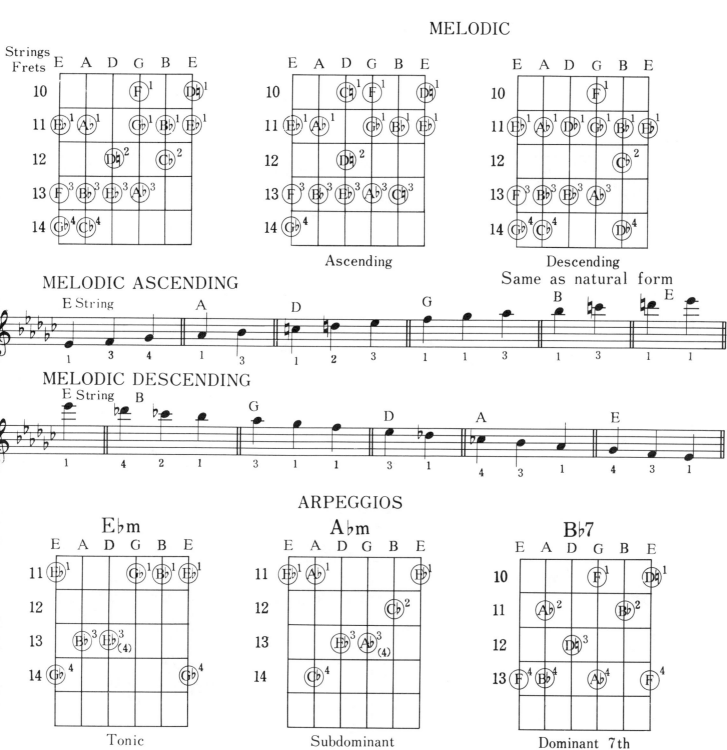

Ascending

Descending
Same as natural form

MELODIC ASCENDING

MELODIC DESCENDING

ARPEGGIOS

E♭m — Tonic

A♭m — Subdominant

B♭7 — Dominant 7th

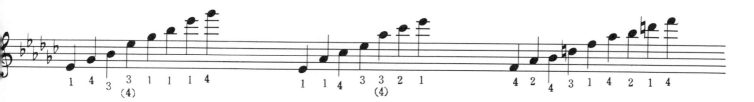

TERTIARY FORMS

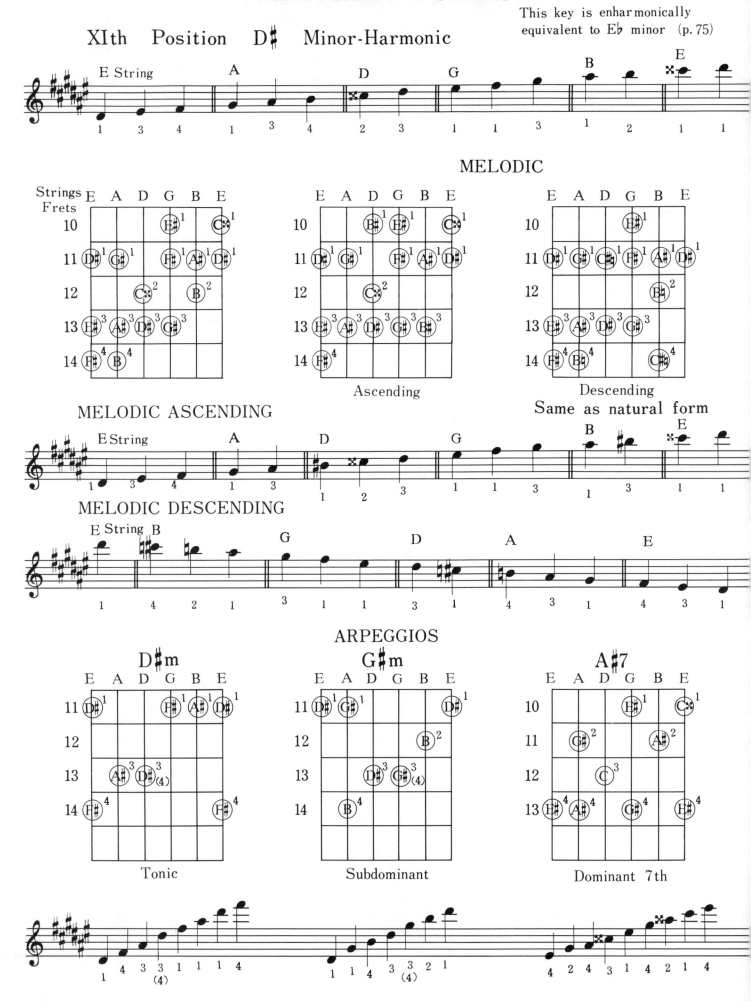

QUATERNARY FORMS

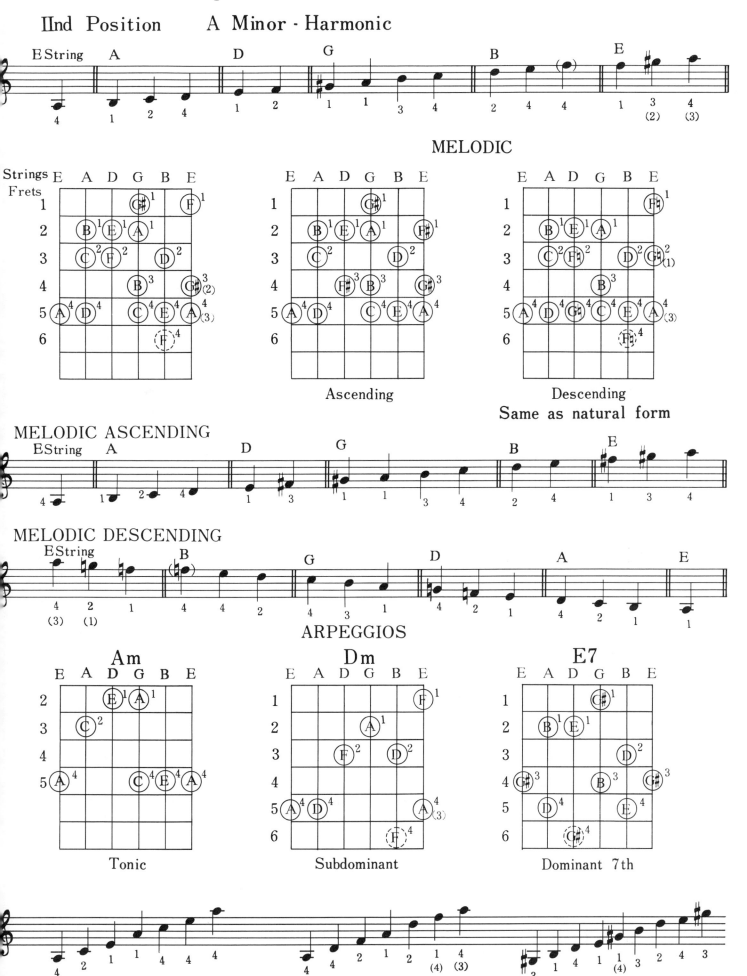

IInd Position   A Minor - Harmonic

MELODIC

Ascending   Descending
Same as natural form

MELODIC ASCENDING

MELODIC DESCENDING

ARPEGGIOS

Am   Dm   E7

Tonic   Subdominant   Dominant 7th

QUATERNARY FORMS

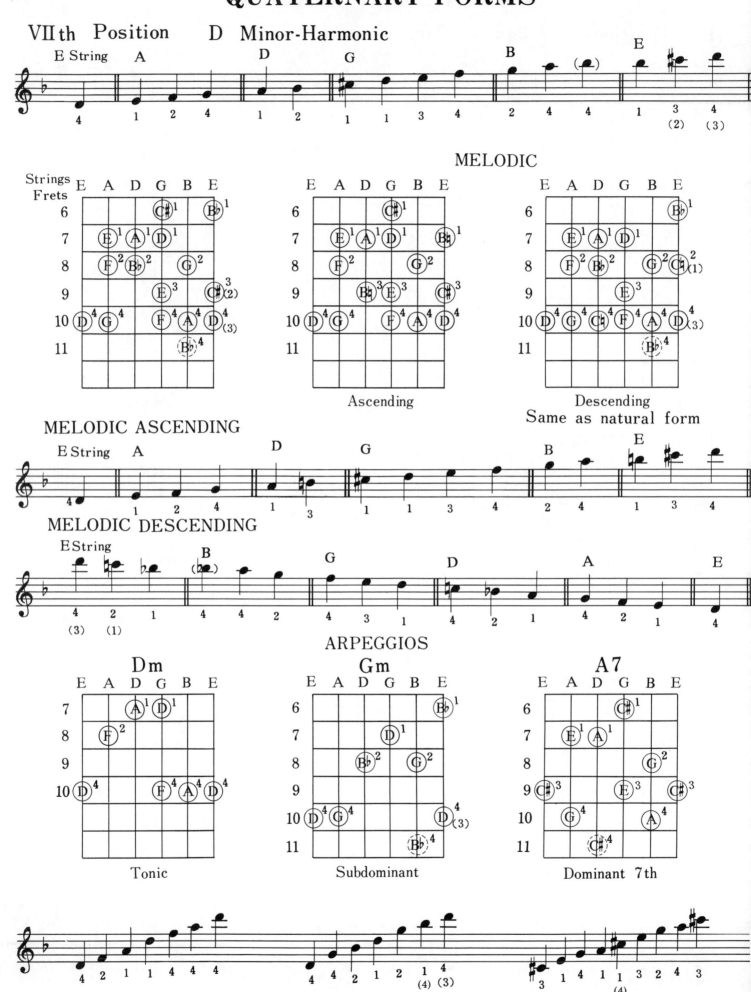

VIIth Position   D Minor-Harmonic

MELODIC

MELODIC ASCENDING

MELODIC DESCENDING

Ascending

Descending
Same as natural form

Strings / Frets

ARPEGGIOS

Dm   Gm   A7

Tonic   Subdominant   Dominant 7th

QUATERNARY FORMS

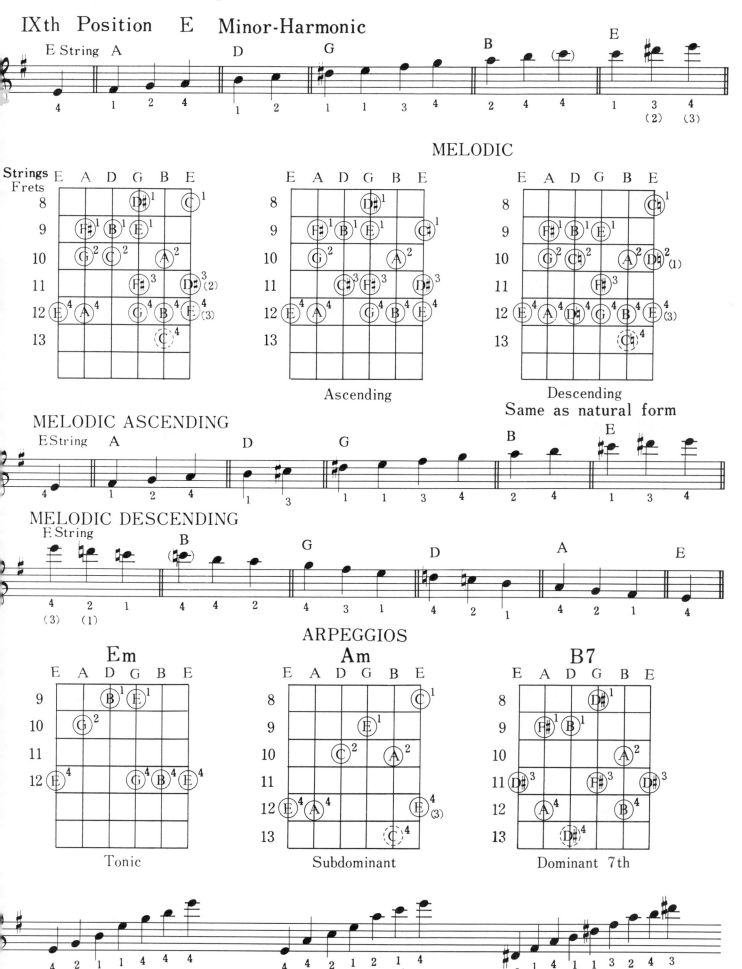

QUATERNARY FORMS

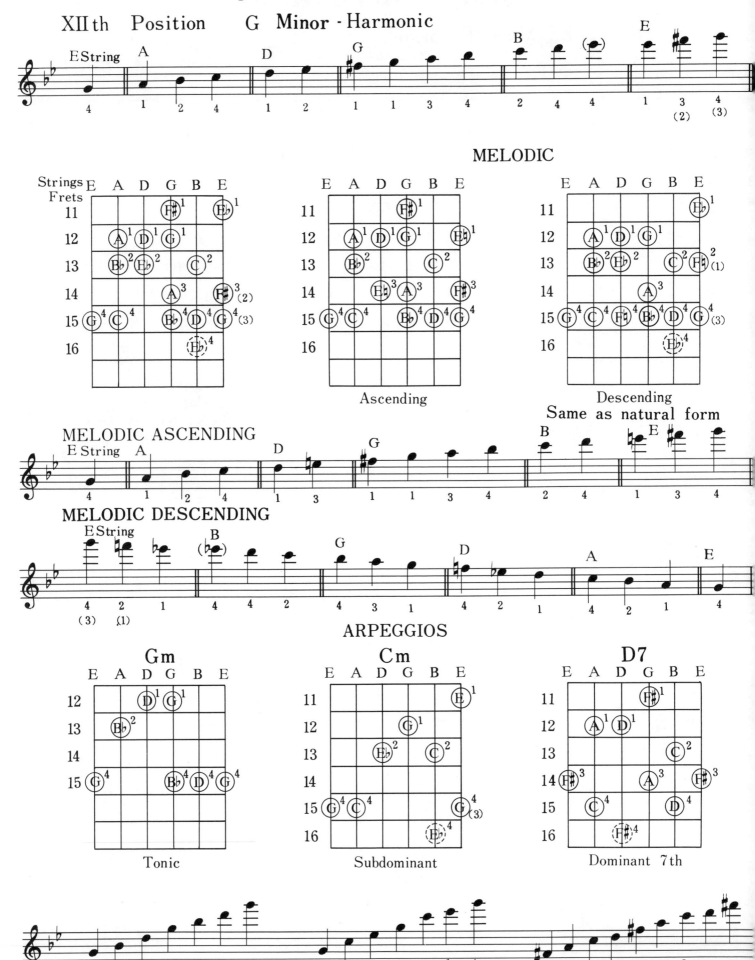

XIIth Position — G Minor - Harmonic

MELODIC

MELODIC ASCENDING

Same as natural form

MELODIC DESCENDING

ARPEGGIOS

Gm — Tonic

Cm — Subdominant

D7 — Dominant 7th

QUATERNARY FORMS

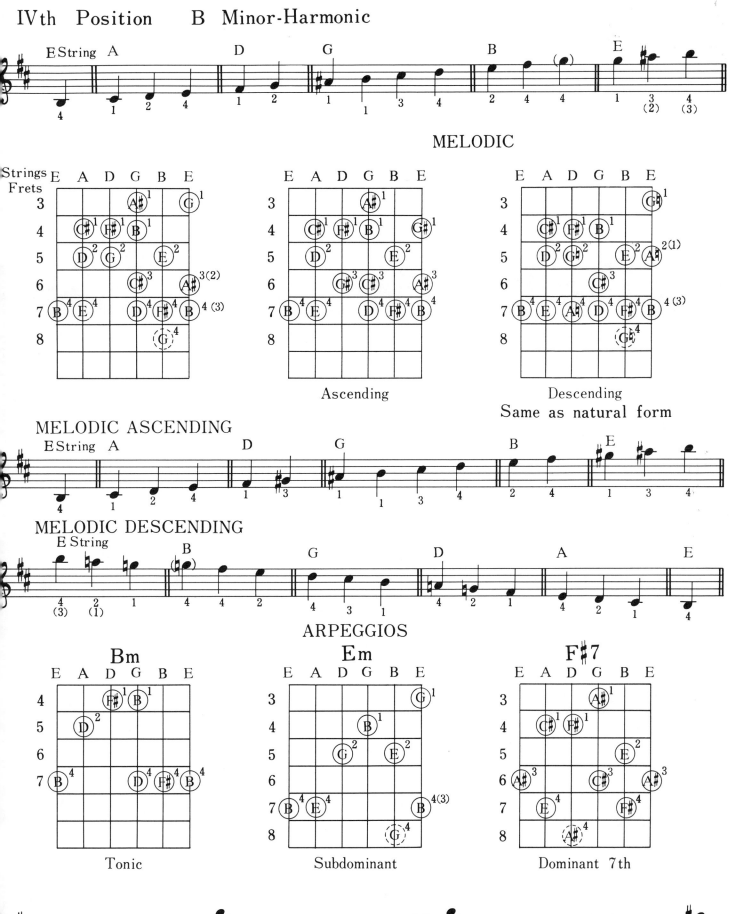

QUATERNARY FORMS

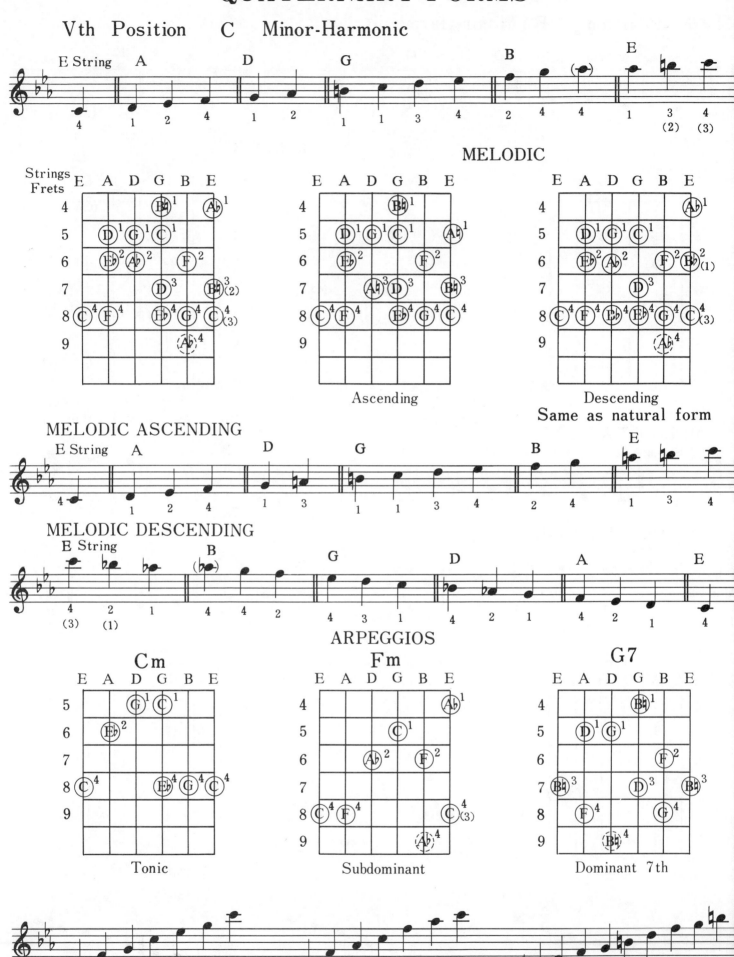

Vth Position   C   Minor-Harmonic

MELODIC

Ascending

Descending
Same as natural form

MELODIC ASCENDING

MELODIC DESCENDING

ARPEGGIOS

Cm

Fm

G 7

Tonic

Subdominant

Dominant 7th

QUATERNARY FORMS

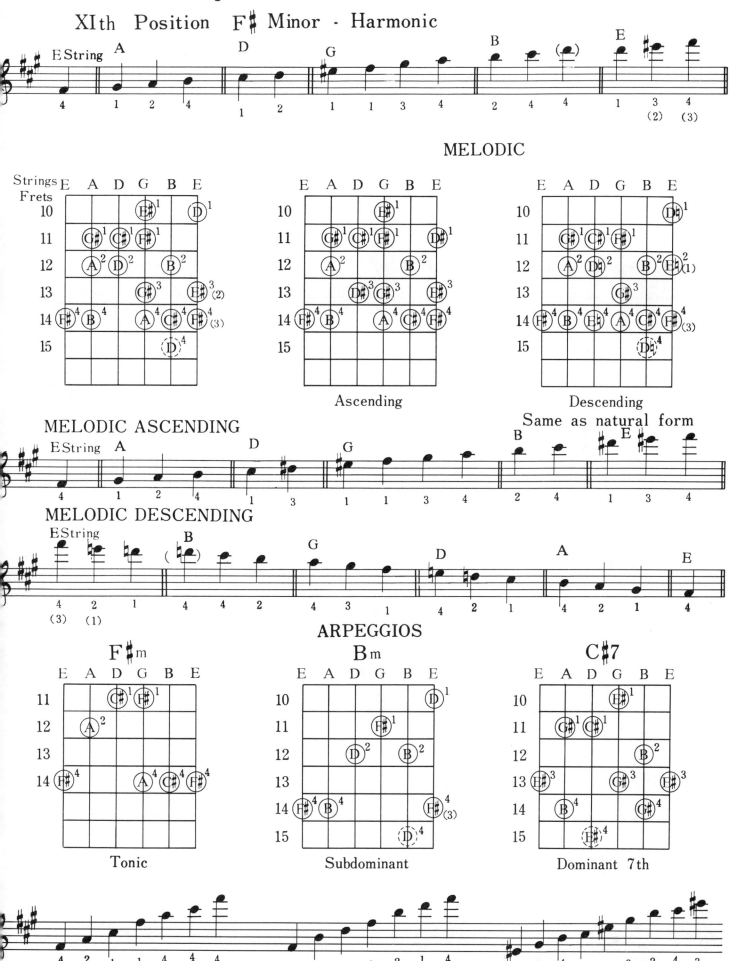

QUATERNARY FORMS

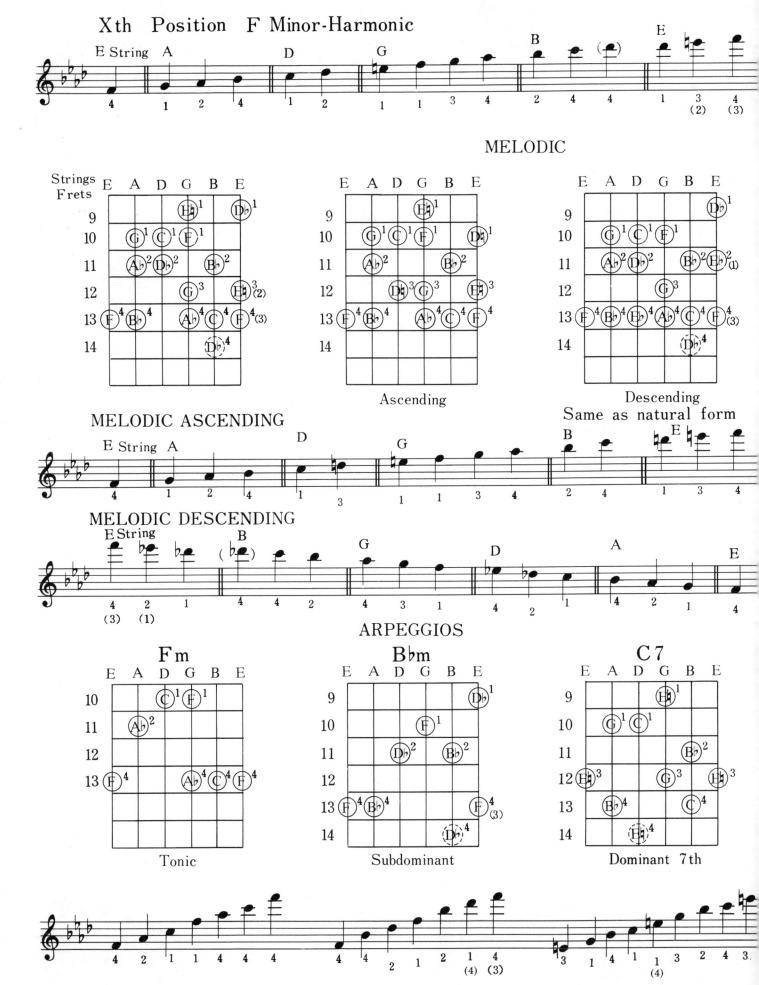

Xth Position F Minor-Harmonic

MELODIC

MELODIC ASCENDING

MELODIC DESCENDING

Ascending

Descending
Same as natural form

ARPEGGIOS

Fm — Tonic

B♭m — Subdominant

C 7 — Dominant 7th

QUATERNARY FORMS

VIth Position   C♯ Minor-Harmonic

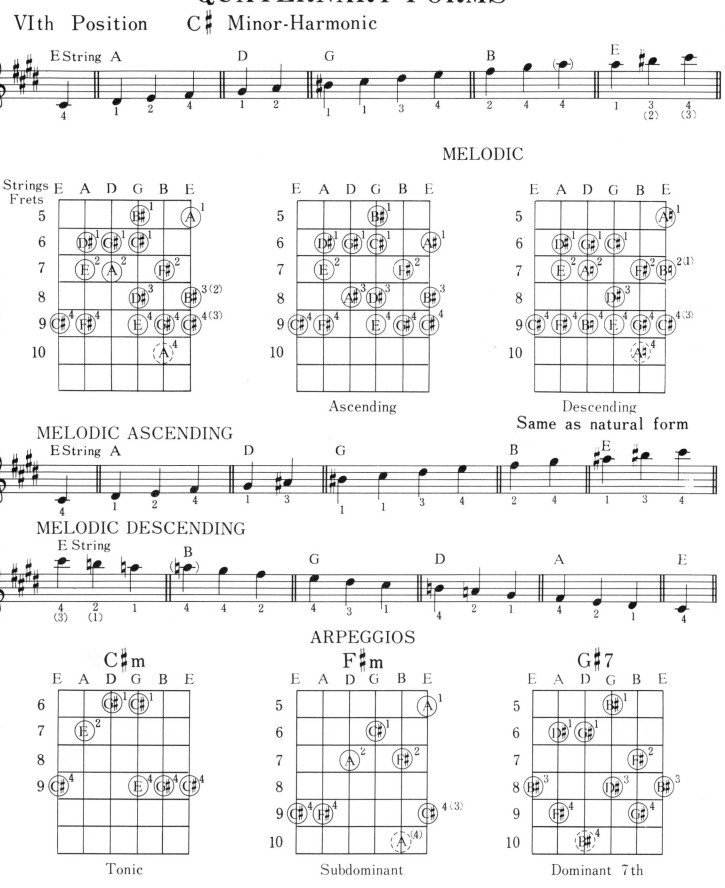

MELODIC

Ascending

Descending
Same as natural form

MELODIC ASCENDING

MELODIC DESCENDING

ARPEGGIOS

C♯m — Tonic

F♯m — Subdominant

G♯7 — Dominant 7th

QUATERNARY FORMS

IIIrd Position   Bb Minor-Harmonic

MELODIC

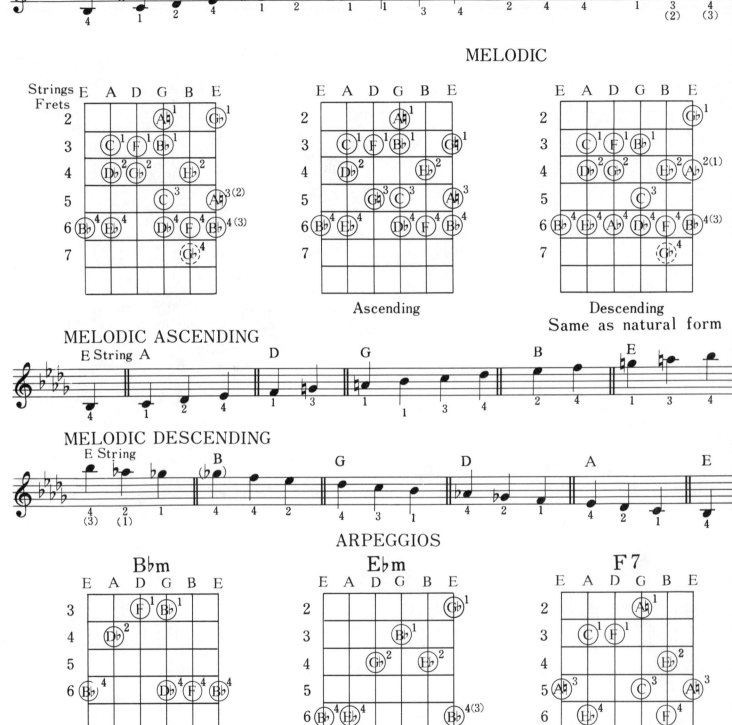

Ascending

Descending
Same as natural form

MELODIC ASCENDING

MELODIC DESCENDING

ARPEGGIOS

Bbm

Ebm

F7

Tonic

Subdominant

Dominant 7th

QUATERNARY FORMS

Ist Position G♯ Minor-Harmonic

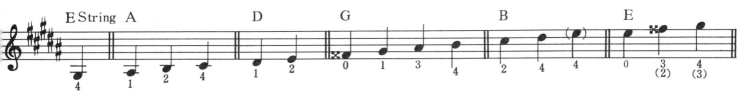

MELODIC

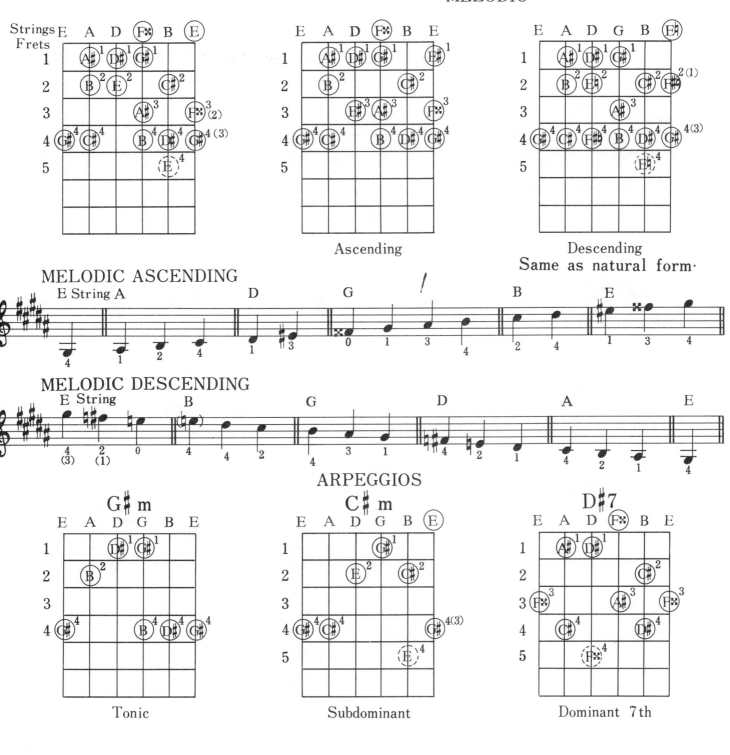

Ascending

Descending
Same as natural form·

MELODIC ASCENDING

MELODIC DESCENDING

ARPEGGIOS

G♯m
Tonic

C♯m
Subdominant

D♯7
Dominant 7th

QUATERNARY FORMS

VIII th Position   Eb Minor-Harmonic

This key is enharmonically equivalent to D♯ minor (p.

MELODIC

Ascending

Descending

Same as natural form

MELODIC ASCENDING

MELODIC DESCENDING

ARPEGGIOS

Ebm — Tonic

Abm — Subdominant

Bb7 — Dominant 7th

QUATERNARY FORMS

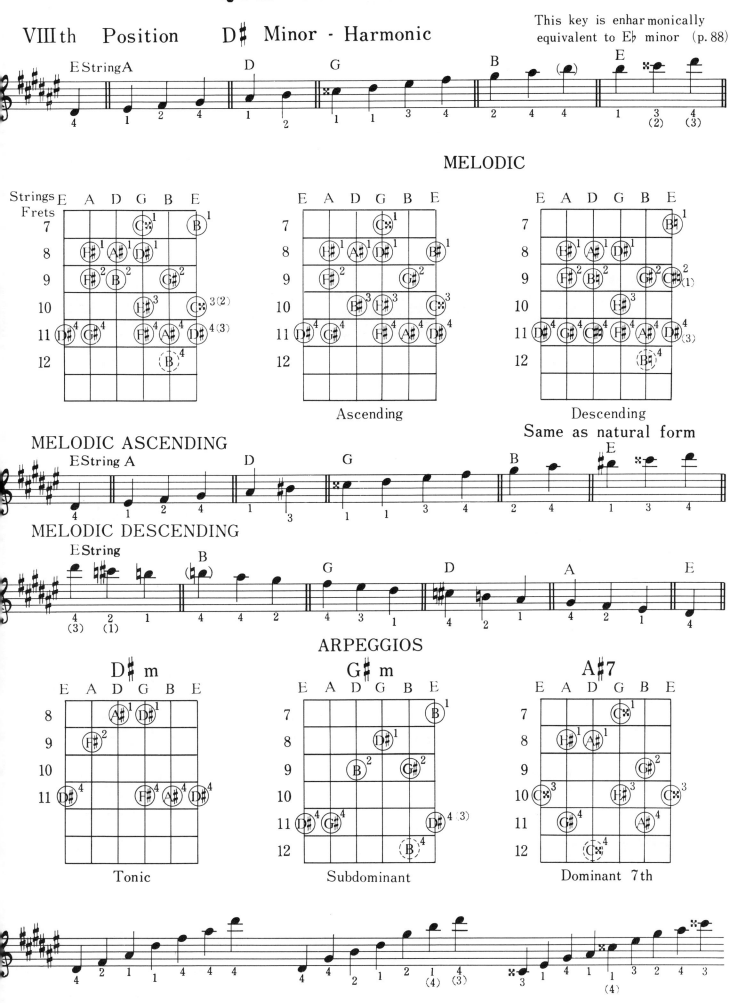

VIIIth Position   D♯ Minor - Harmonic   This key is enharmonically equivalent to E♭ minor (p. 88)

MELODIC

Ascending

Descending

Same as natural form

MELODIC ASCENDING

MELODIC DESCENDING

ARPEGGIOS

D♯m   G♯m   A♯7

Tonic   Subdominant   Dominant 7th

SPECIAL SCALES

THE CHROMATIC SCALE

The chromatic scale is playable in any position. It is here demonstrated in the 5th position and notated in the key of C major.

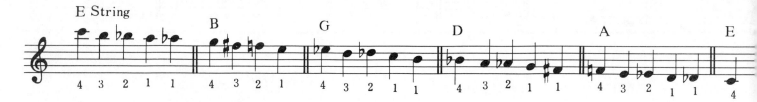

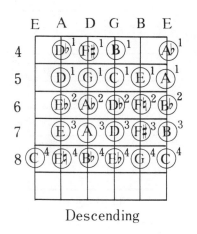

Descending

The choice of fingering will depend on the context of the composition. The player should be able to play scales, or parts of scales, in any of the presented forms.

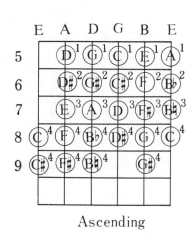

Ascending

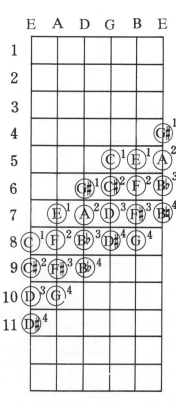

This form of the chromatic scale leaves position, but it has the advantage of simplified fingering and might be easier to play when the range of the scale is more than a few notes.

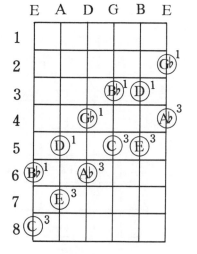

Whole Tone Scale

PART THREE - COMPREHENSIVE ARPEGGIOS
MAJOR TRIAD

Construct each arpeggio on the given bass using the F major model.

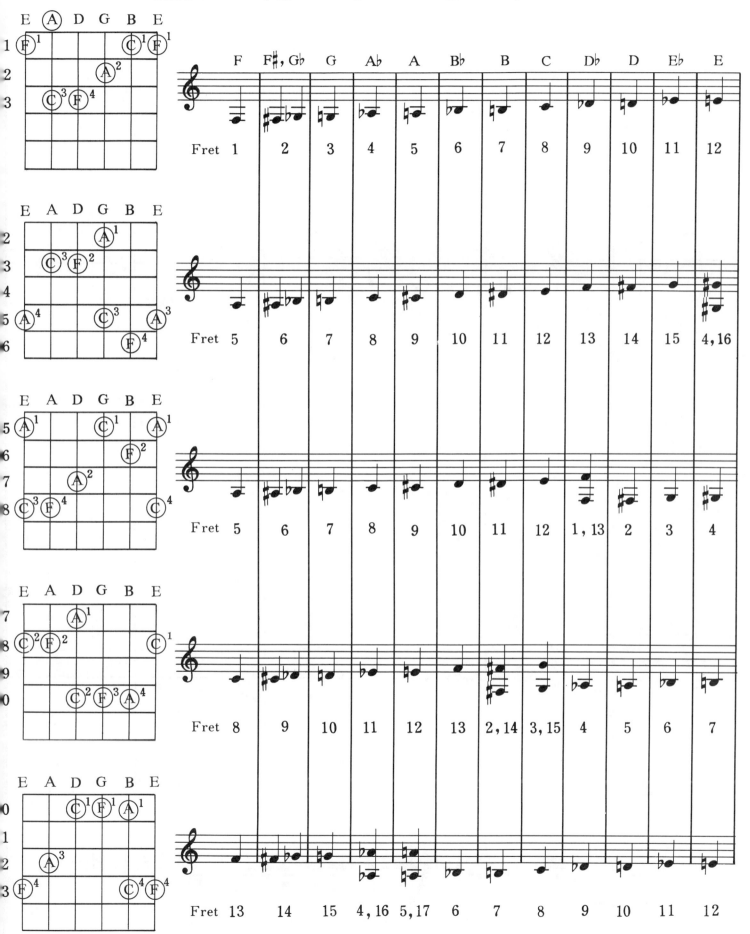

MINOR TRIAD

Construct each arpeggio on the given bass using the D minor model.

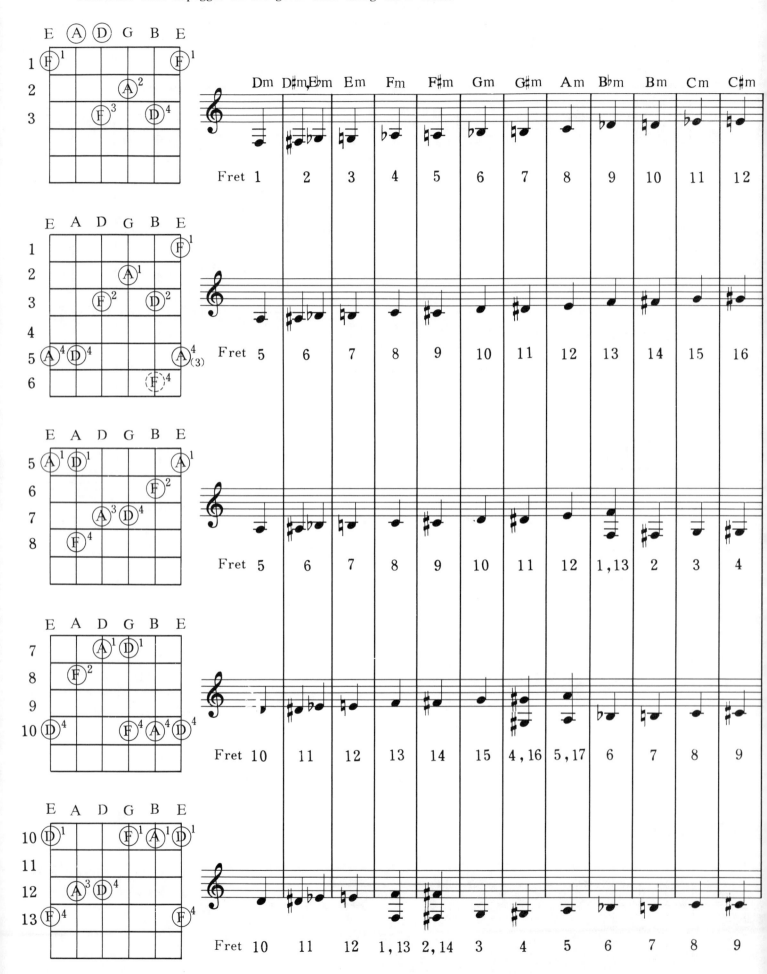

DOMINANT 7th

Construct each arpeggio on the given bass using the C7 model.

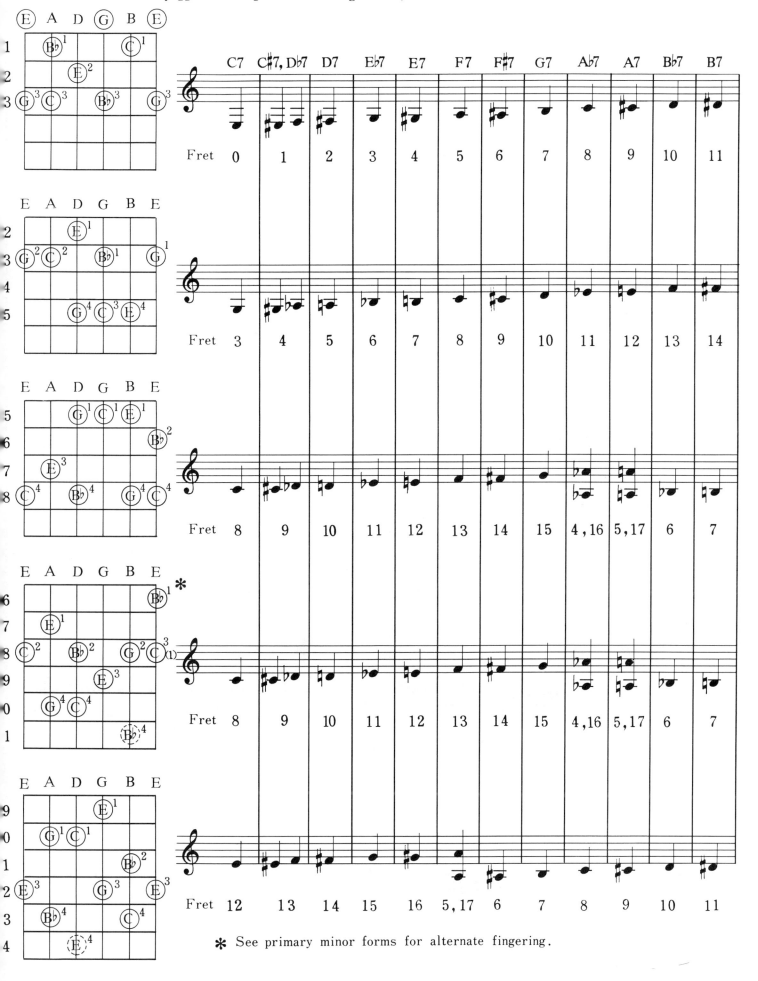

* See primary minor forms for alternate fingering.

94

MINOR 7th OR MAJOR 6th

The minor 7th arpeggio and the major 6th arpeggio (one minor 3rd higher) have the same spelling.
Construct each arpeggio on the given bass using the F6, Dm7 model.

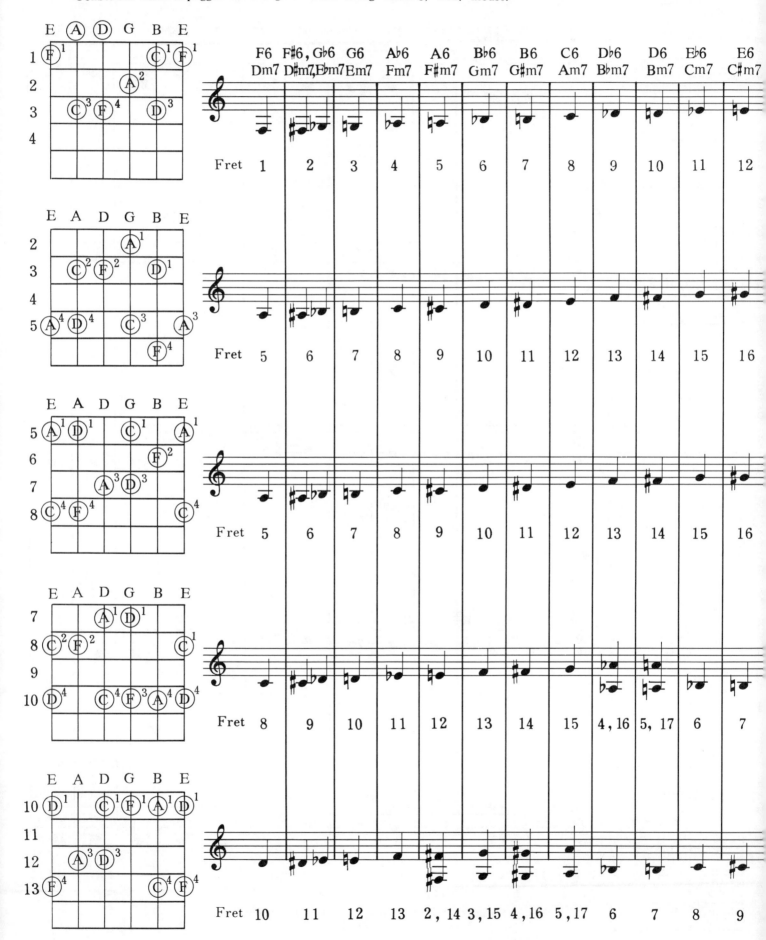

MINOR 6th

Construct each arpeggio on the given bass using the Dm6 model.

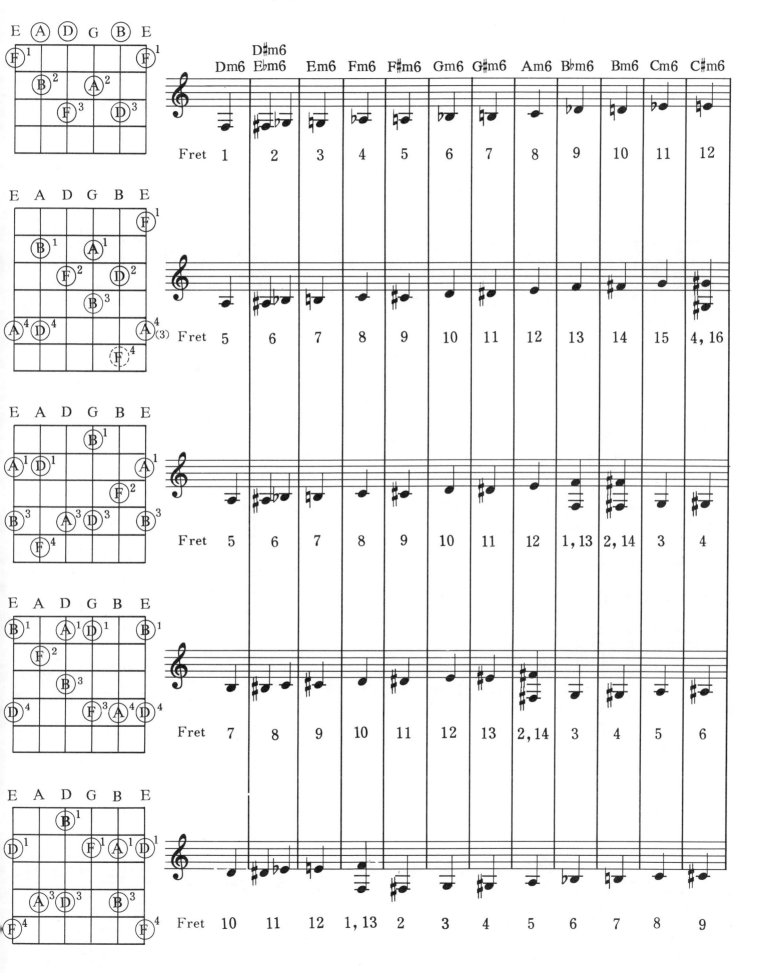

MAJOR 7th

Construct each arpeggio on the given bass using the F maj7 model.

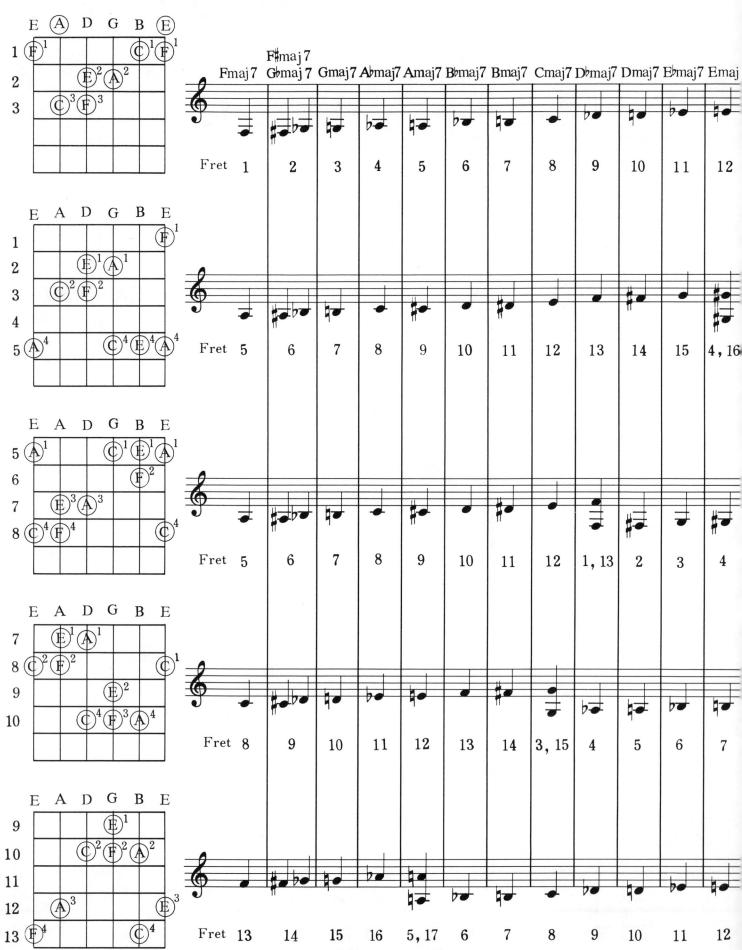

DIMINISHED 7th

The diminished 7th arpeggio derives its name from any one of the notes contained in the arpeggio. Each note has an enharmonic equivalent. For example, C♭ = B, E♭♭ = D. Each diminished 7th arpeggio is repeatable every third fret (1½ tones) up the fingerboard.

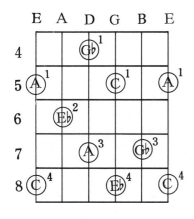

These forms were presented by the authors many years ago in Guitar Melody Playing (1948). They are still very useful. The following form is presented as a variation and perhaps easier to visualize.

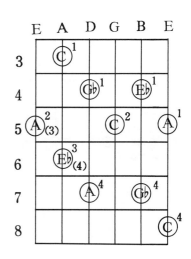

Fdim7, A♭dim7, Bdim7, Ddim7

F♯dim7, Adim7, Cdim7, E♭dim7

Gdim7, B♭dim7, D♭dim7, Edim7

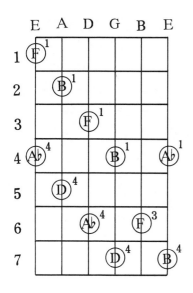

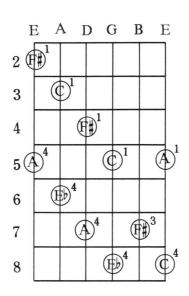

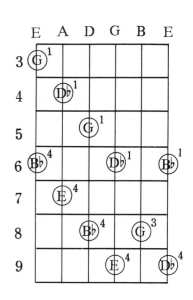

AUGMENTED 5th TRIAD

The augmented 5th triad arpeggio derives its name from any one of the notes contained in the arpeggio. Each note has an enharmonic equivalent. For example, A♭ = G♯ , F = E♯. Each augmented 5th triad arpeggio is repeatable every fourth fret(2 tones) up the fingerboard.

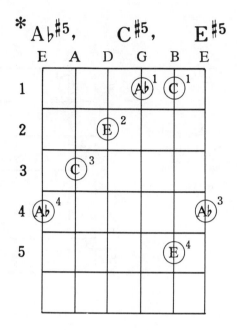

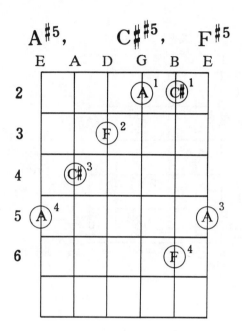

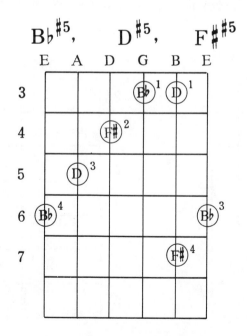

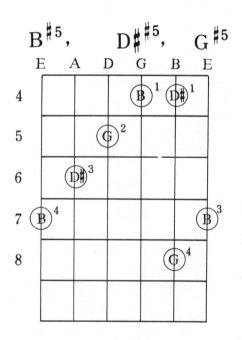

✻ Sometimes Notated A♭ + 5, or simply A♭ + .

DOMINANT 7th #5

Any dominant 7th arpeggio may be altered to include a sharped 5th. Construct the dominant 7#5 arpeggio in all the keys from the models shown.

C7#5

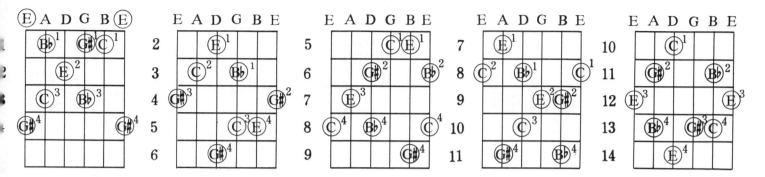

DOMINANT 7th ♭5

Similary, any dominant 7th arpeggio may be altered to include a flatted 5th. Construct the dominant 7♭5 arpeggio in all the keys from the models shown.

C7♭5

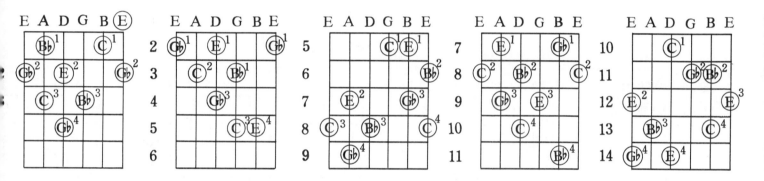

DOMINANT 9th

Construct the dominant 9th arpeggio in all the keys from the models shown.

C9

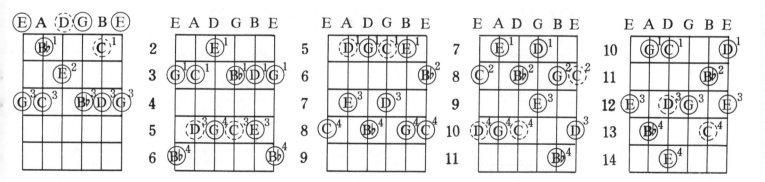

The more notes in a chord or arpeggio, the more it may require careful voicing. The dominant 9th above may sound better if some notes are skipped in the total progression. For example, the root may be played but once and skipped in the upper range. Similarly, the 9th, 11th, and 13th may be skipped in the lower range. The arpeggios to follow will be voiced in such a manner.

MAJOR 7th ♭3

Construct the major 7♭3 arpeggio in all the keys from the models shown.

F maj7♭3

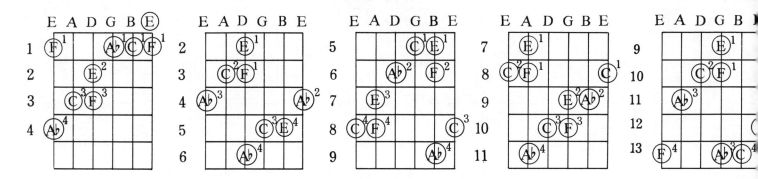

MINOR 7th ♭5

Construct the minor 7♭5 arpeggio in all the keys from the models shown.

Dm7♭5

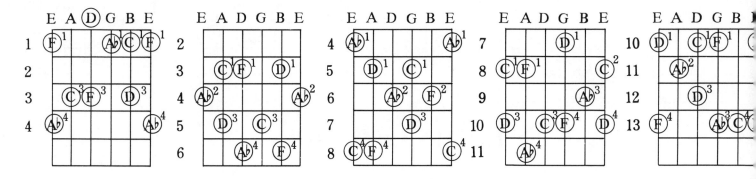

DOMINANT 7th SUSPEND 4

Construct the dominant 7th suspend 4 in all the keys from the models shown.

C7 sus 4

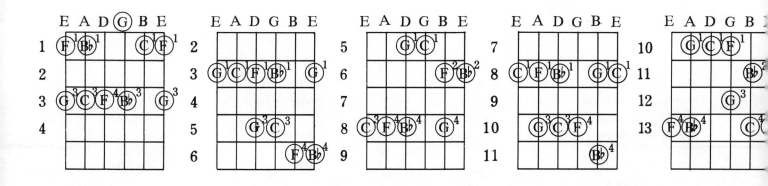

MINOR 9th

Construct the minor 9th in all the keys from the models shown.

Dm9

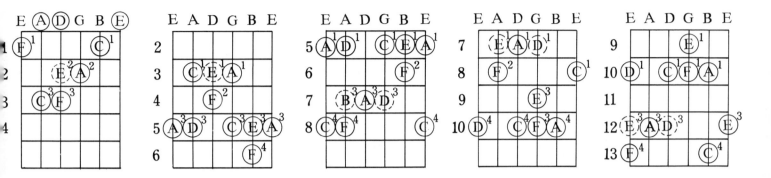

MAJOR 9th

Construct the major 9th in all the keys from the models shown.

F maj9

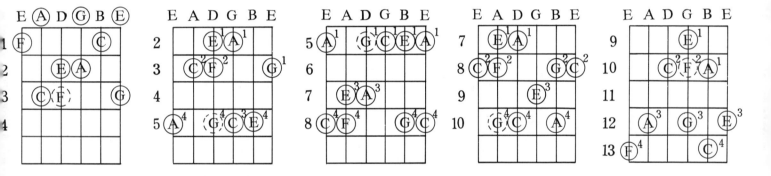

DOMINANT 9th ♯5

Construct the dominant 9th ♯5 in all the keys from the models shown.

C9♯5

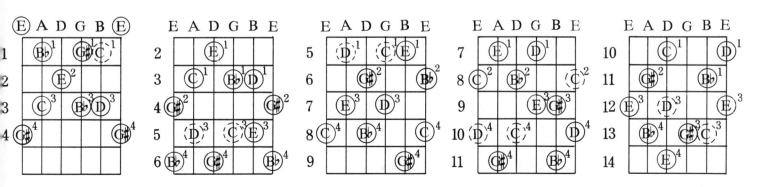

DOMINANT 9th ♭5

Construct the dominant 9th ♭5 arpeggio in all the keys from the models shown.

C 9♭5

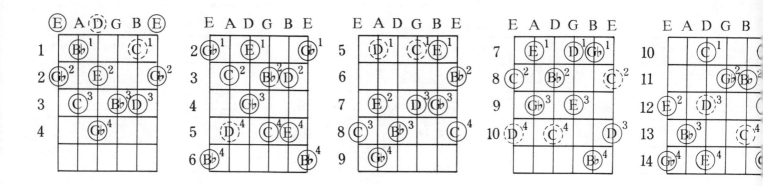

DOMINANT 7th ♭9

Construct the dominant 7th ♭9 arpeggio in all the keys from the models shown.

C 7♭9

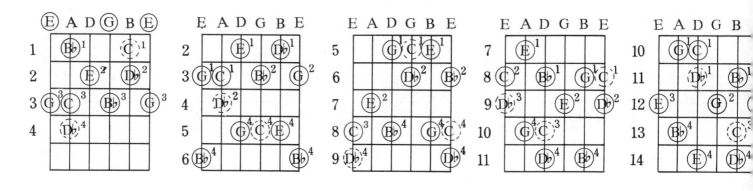

DOMINANT 7th ♯9

Construct the dominant 7th ♯9 arpeggio in all the keys from the models shown.

C 7♯9

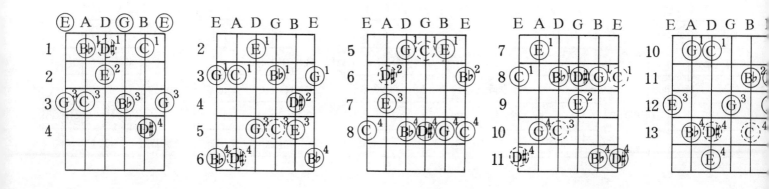

MAJOR 6th add 9

Construct the major 6th add 9 arpeggio in all the keys from the models shown.

F 6 add 9

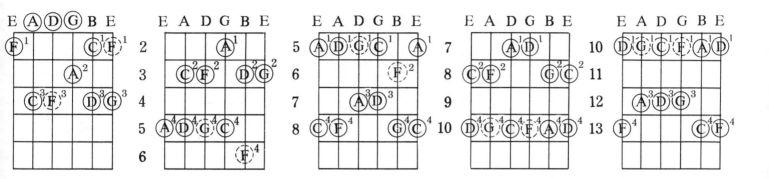

DOMINANT 11th

Construct the dominant 11th arpeggio in all the keys from the models shown.

C 11

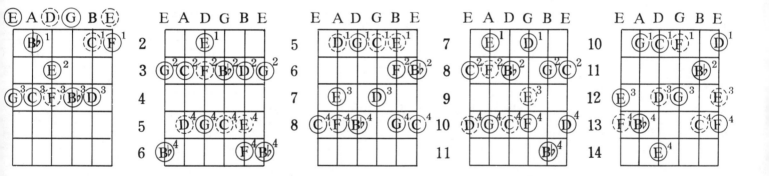

DOMINANT 7th ♯11

Construct the dominant 7th ♯ 11 arpeggio in all the keys from the models shown.

C 7♯11

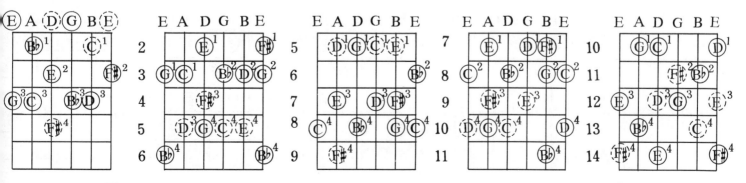

(This arpeggio looks very much like it was lifted right out of " Natures Scale ".)

DOMINANT 13th

Construct the dominant 13th arpeggio in all the keys from the models shown.
(Simplified for clarity.)

C13

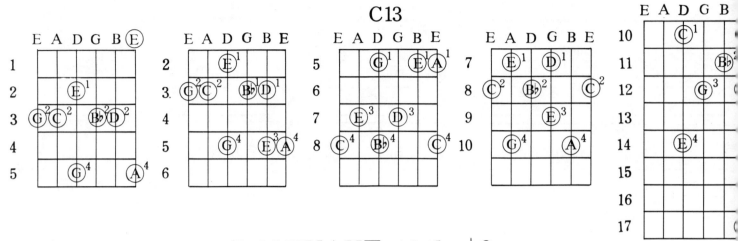

DOMINANT 13th ♭9

Construct the dominant 13th ♭9 arpeggio in all the keys from the models shown.

C13♭9

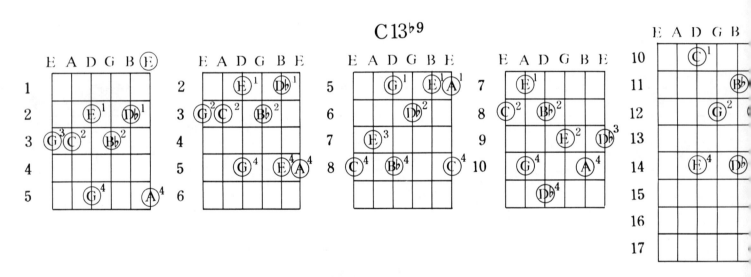

DOMINANT 13th ♭5 ♭9

Construct the dominant 13th ♭5 ♭9 arpeggio in the keys from the models shown.

C13♭5♭9

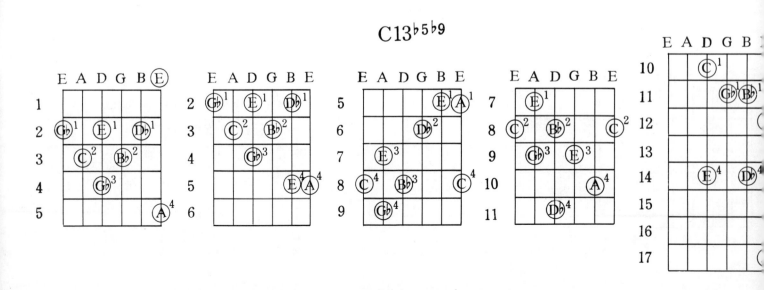